Developing SPANISH

PHOTOCOPIABLE LANGUAGE ACTIVITIES FOR BEGINNERS

Anna Grassi and
Cristina Kollinger Collesei

BLOOMSBURY EDUCATION
AN IMPRINT OF BLOOMSBURY
LONDON OXFORD NEW YORK NEW DELHI SYDNEY

For Rupali, Tommaso, Fleck and Selva

First published 2007 by A & C Black Publishers Limited
Published 2016 by Bloomsbury Education
an imprint of Bloomsbury Publishing Plc
50 Bedford Square
London
WC1B 3DP

www.bloomsbury.com
ISBN: 978-0-7136-7930-4

Editor: Jane Klima
Design: Susan McIntyre

The authors and publishers would like to thank Lindsay Blundell and Sarah Potter for their assistance in producing this book.

A CIP catalogue record for this book is available from the British Library.

Printed in India by Replika Press Pvt. Ltd.

This book is produced using paper that is made from wood grown in managed, sustainable forests. It is natural, renewable and recyclable. The logging and manufacturing processes conform to the environmental regulations of the country of origin.

Contents

Introduction

Developing Spanish has been designed in line with the Key Stage 2 *Framework for languages* of the National Languages Strategy and offers opportunities to develop and extend the main learning objectives, including:

Oracy

- Identifying key words and phrases in short passages of spoken Spanish;
- Asking and answering questions on a range of topics;
- Engaging in simple conversations and beginning to use language imaginatively.

Literacy

- Reading a variety of short texts;
- Creating simple texts for different purposes;
- Learning about the basic writing system, the spelling and the structure of Spanish.

Intercultural understanding

- Learning about aspects of Spanish culture and traditions through comparisons with their own culture;
- Recognising similarities and differences between people.

Knowledge about language (KAL)

- Reflecting on linguistic similarities and differences such as sounds, the written word, phrasing and sentence order between Spanish and English.

Language learning strategies (LLS)

- Providing teachers with examples of learning strategies to help the children to learn and to retain Spanish.

Teaching requirements

The teaching suggestions and learning activities in **Developing Spanish** may be integrated into classroom lessons or used during after-school clubs or by parents at home. Ideally, all teaching should be in Spanish, but this is not essential – the books are written so that they can be used by a non-native speaker if necessary. Translations are provided for all key vocabulary and each book includes a guide to Spanish pronunciation.

The activities require very few resources beyond pencils, crayons, scissors, card and other general classroom items. Any other materials you will need are specified in the **Notes on the activities** (for example, pictures from magazines, travel brochures, etc.).

Pronunciation

Spanish is a phonetic language – each letter or combination of letters once mastered is always pronounced the same. Most of the Spanish alphabet sounds the same as the English alphabet, but there are some notable exceptions and a few extra letters which have to be learned. You will find all the guidance you need to these and other basic sounds in Spanish in the pronunciation guide on page 8.

Developing Spanish focuses on Spanish as spoken in Spain. Pronunciation variations exist between Iberian Spanish and Latin American Spanish and even between some regions within Spain. For example, *cena* and *cine*, which start with a 'th' sound in most of Spain, are pronounced with an initial 's' sound in Latin America and in some Spanish regions such as Andalucía (Andalusia) and Canarias (the Canary Islands).

The five topics are:

- greetings: introducing oneself;
- school life: classroom objects and routine;
- family life: family members and relationships;
- at home: rooms and furniture, pets;
- outdoor activities: sports and hobbies.

Topics

Each of the five topics includes:

- **key vocabulary, expressions and grammar** – these are listed along with their translation;
- **teaching ideas** to help you to make the most of the topic – these provide suggestions for games, songs, rhymes and role-plays, as well as notes on Spanish culture;
- **notes on the activities** for all the individual photocopiable sheets – these offer introductory or warm-up ideas, suggestions for follow-up work, and page-specific grammar notes where necessary;
- **photocopiable activity sheets**.

Additionally, Topics 2, 3, 4 and 5 conclude with a double-page **picture dictionary**.

Photocopiable activity sheets

There are up to eight photocopiable activity sheets for each topic. Each sheet features:

- a relevant, active vocabulary title;
- instructions and text in simple, clear Spanish with easy-to-recognise activity icons;
- word banks to help the children to carry out the task where appropriate;
- appealing illustrations of typically Spanish objects, situations and scenes. The main characters are a Spanish boy and girl, Carlos and Marta, who appear throughout the series. A number of Carlos and Marta's friends and relatives also feature in the activity sheets;

Carlos

Marta

- a **Teachers' note** at the foot of the page, which may be masked before photocopying.

The teachers' note includes:

- translation of the page title and instructions, and, following a bullet point (•), of the extension task;
- the learning objective;
- a summary of the language skills and vocabulary the children will need to practise before using the sheet;
- advice on how to use the activity sheet.

Most activity sheets end with a challenge (***Y ahora*** – And now…), a writing or speaking activity which aims to reinforce language learned in the main activity and to help the children to become more confident and independent in its use. A notebook or separate sheet of paper will be required for the children to complete some of these extension activities, or they could use the back of the sheet.

Key to the activity icons

The Spanish verbs used in the instructions following the activity icons are in the imperative (command) form of the second person singular (the informal *tú*).

 Mira (Look)

 *Lee* (Read)

 *Escribe* (Write)

 *Dibuja* (Draw)

 *Colorea* (Colour)

 *Habla* (Speak)

 *Escoge* (Choose)

 *Busca* (Find)

 *Corta* (Cut)

 *Pega* (Glue)

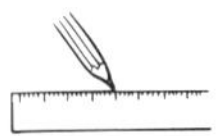 *Une* (Join)

Ordena (Order)

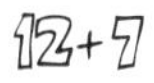

Cuenta (Count)

 *Juega* (Play)

Picture dictionaries

These four illustrated spreads feature a title and 22 vocabulary words. The border illustrations represent nouns if they are inside a circle, verbs if they are inside a square and adjectives if they are inside an octagon. This distinction can be used as a learning strategy to help the children to reflect on the structure of language.

las tijeras

dormir

contento/a

The picture dictionaries can be used in a number of ways:

- To introduce and/or revise written and spoken vocabulary. Mask the words and give each child a copy. Ask the children to write the names or to say the words in Spanish.
- To revise grammar. Mask the articles and ask the children to write them in or to say them aloud. The children can also identify the gender of words by using different coloured highlighters or by underlining or circling words.
- For a variety of spoken games and activities such as counting, describing, guessing and finding. For example, ask the children *¿Cuántos alumnos hay en la clase?* (How many pupils are there in the class?) or *¿Quién es alto?* (Which person is tall?) or *¿Dónde está el libro?* (Where is the book?)

Additional suggestions for using the picture dictionaries are provided in the corresponding topic's teaching ideas.

Recommended resources

Recommended suppliers of Spanish books and teaching materials, suggested websites for teachers and for children, and details of curriculum information and teaching methods are listed on page 62.

Answers

Turn to pages 63 and 64 for answers to all the questions, wordsearches, puzzles and crosswords featured on the activity sheets.

Pull-out frieze

Inside the back cover is an appealing giant colour pull-out frieze to be displayed in the classroom. The frieze presents a Spanish scene with 20 key words, including verbs, dotted around the illustration. Words in rounded boxes are nouns; words in rectangular boxes are verbs.

You can use the frieze as a warm-up at the beginning of each lesson to revise vocabulary and as a short conversation starter. For example, ask individual children questions about the frieze such as *¿Dónde está el niño?* (Where is the boy?), then follow up with a supplementary question about themselves: *Y tú, ¿dónde estás?* (And what about you – where are you?)

As with the picture dictionaries, the shape code may be used as a learning strategy. Go over the words on the frieze and discuss their function according to whether they are in a rounded box or in a rectangular box. Draw two different large shapes on the board, one for nouns and one for verbs. Ask the children to think of either a noun or a verb and to write it on a post-it note. They should then exchange their slips of paper, take turns to read them aloud and stick them in the correct shape on the board.

General teaching suggestions

One of the keys to success in learning a foreign language is constant practice. The activities contained in **Developing Spanish** offer plenty of opportunities for varied and differentiated practice.

Here are some extra suggestions on how to help the children to learn and to practise new vocabulary:

Drills and repetition are useful for pronunciation practice and to help the children to memorise words. For example, prompt the children to repeat words *lentamente* (slowly), *rápidamente* (quickly), *susurrando* (in a whisper), *fuerte* (loudly), etc.

Pairs of children could practise vocabulary by taking turns to count or find the opposites of adjectives or by playing word association games. The gender of nouns can be reinforced by one child saying the noun and his or her partner supplying the definite or indefinite article.

Oral games and **role-play activities** encourage the children to become more comfortable with the language. An example of a simple oral word game is

La maleta (Suitcase) where the first child says *Voy a Madrid y llevo un gato* (I'm going to Madrid and I'm taking a cat). The second child repeats the sentence and adds a second word. The third child repeats the sentence and adds a third word and so on.

Playing *El ahorcado* (Hangman) is a quick way for the children to revise vocabulary and spelling.

Another popular game is *Veo, veo* (I spy). This is useful for practising colours:

A: *Veo, veo.*
B: *¿Qué ves?*
A: *Veo una cosa amarilla.*
B: *¿El sol?*
A: *¡No!*
B: *¿El plátano?*
A: *¡No!*
B: *¿El libro?*
A: *¡Sí!*

The oral game *¡Qué confusión!* (What a muddle!) can be adapted to fit a variety of scenarios: for example, school subjects, parts of the house, where things are, etc. Feed the children a piece of false information or one incorrect word or phrase in a series of correct phrases. The first child to realise shouts *¡Qué confusión!* and has the chance to say the correct information instead.

The children will also enjoy miming action verbs and preparing simple sketches or role-plays. Use the dialogues presented in the activity sheets for ideas.

Card games such as Pelmanism (Pairs) and Snap! using flashcards are a fun way for the children to consolidate vocabulary. Pelmanism can be played individually, in pairs, or even as a whole class with enlarged cards. When playing Snap!, the children must call out the Spanish word on the card instead of the word 'Snap!'

Another important element in learning a foreign language is a comfortable learning environment. Use Spanish as much as possible along with a variety of teaching styles. It is helpful to establish a routine at the beginning of every lesson so that the children know what to expect. Always exchange greetings in the same way at the start of each session. The beginning of a lesson is a good time to review previously introduced material through drills and questions.

Praise and encouragement in Spanish also help to foster a relaxed learning atmosphere. Some useful expressions are *¡Excelente!* (Excellent!), *¡Muy bien!* (Very good!), *¡Buen trabajo!* (Good work!), *¡Perfecto!* (Perfect!)

A stimulating learning environment can be attained by displaying the children's work, the **Developing Spanish** pull-out friezes, enlarged copies of the picture dictionaries, posters, a *¡Bienvenidos!* (Welcome!) sign, etc. Use real-life visual aids such as Spanish travel posters and brochures, postcards, banknotes, coins, menus, train tickets and product labels for the children to touch and see. Laminating visual aids will help to extend their life.

An effective way to boost the children's confidence in their oral abilities is to organise a 'show' of what they have learned for parents and/or schoolmates. They could perform short sketches that they have written themselves, or they could play an oral game in teams. For instance, you could divide the class into two teams lined up at one end of the room. At the other end set up a box full of colourful clothes and another box of slips of paper with the names and colours of the items of clothing written on them: for example, *Una bufanda naranja* (An orange scarf) or *Un sombrero verde* (A green hat). To play, the first child in each team runs to the box of slips, takes one, runs back and reads it aloud to the next child in his or her team. The second child runs to find the named item in the clothes box and puts it on over whatever he or she is already wearing. Once it is on properly, he or she picks another slip and runs back to tell the next person in line what to choose from the clothes box. The last person in the team has to tell the first person in line what to put on. The winners are the team who are first to be all wearing an item of clothing from the box.

Pronunciation guide

This page offers guidance on how to pronounce all the basic sounds of letters or combinations of letters in Spanish. Where possible, an English word containing the approximate sound is given for each one. Practise the sound by reading the practice words aloud several times.

You may want to ask a native Spanish speaker or a Spanish-language teacher to help you with the correct pronunciation.

Note that both the guide below and the online guide reflect the pronunciation of Spanish as spoken in most of Spain. Pronunciation variations may be found in Latin American countries and in some regions of Spain.

a like the 'a' sound in 'bad'
practice words: *la, casa, mamá*

e like the 'e' sound in 'get'
practice words: *el, tres, tener*

i like the 'ee' sound in 'feet', but shorter
practice words: *bici, mira, venir*

o like the 'o' sound in 'box'
practice words: *no, moto, color*

u like the 'oo' sound in 'tooth'
practice words: *una, usar, tu*

c like the 'c' sound in 'cat' except before e or *i*
practice words: *café, comer, cubo*

like the 'th' sound in 'thin' when before e or *i*
practice words: *cena, centro, cine*

ch like the 'ch' sound in 'church'
practice words: *mucho, ducha, coche*

g like the 'g' sound in 'go' except before e or *i*
practice words: *gato, goma, regalo*

like the 'ch' sound in 'loch' when before e or *i*
practice words: *gente, gimnasio*

gu like the 'g' sound in 'go' when before e or *i* (the *u* is silent)
practice words: *guerra, guitarra*

h is always silent
practice words: *hacer, hermano*

j like the 'ch' sound in 'loch'
practice words: *jamón, jugar, jugo*

ll depending on the region, like the 'lli' sound in 'million' or like the 'y' sound in 'yes'
practice words: *calle, silla, llama*

ñ like the 'ni' sound in 'onion'
practice words: *niño, baño, mañana*

q like the 'k' sound in 'kite' (it is always followed by a silent *u*)
practice words: *que, querer, quince*

r a softly trilled 'r' sound like a Scottish *r*
practice words: *hora, mira*

a strongly trilled 'r' sound when it's the first letter of a word
practice words: *rana, ropa*

rr a strongly trilled 'r' sound
practice words: *corre, aburrido*

v like the 'b' sound in 'boy'
practice words: *ver, vivir*

y like the 'y' sound in 'yes'
practice words: *yo, yogur*

z like the 'th' sound in 'think'
practice words: *zapato, zorro, luz*

Topic 1: ¡Empecemos!

Key vocabulary

¡Empecemos!	Let's begin!
un amigo/una amiga	friend
un chico	boy
una chica	girl
un niño	young boy
una niña	young girl
un hombre	man
una mujer	woman
los colores	colours
amarillo/a	yellow
azul	blue
blanco/a	white
celeste	light blue
gris	grey
marrón	brown
morado/a	purple
naranja	orange
negro/a	black
rojo/a	red
rosado/a	pink
verde	green
los números	numbers

numbers 0 to 10: *cero* (0), *uno* (1), *dos* (2), *tres* (3), *cuatro* (4), *cinco* (5), *seis* (6), *siete* (7), *ocho* (8), *nueve* (9), *diez* (10)

Expressions

¡Hola!	Hello!
¿Cómo te llamas?	What's your name?
Yo me llamo…	My name is…
¿Y tú?	And you?
¡Adiós!	Goodbye!
Hasta luego	See you later
Buenos días	Good morning
Buenas tardes	Good afternoon
Buenas noches	Good evening/ Good night
¿Cómo estás/está?	How are you?
(Muy) bien, gracias.	Fine, thank you.
¿Cuál es tu número de teléfono?	What is your telephone number?
Mi número es…	My number is…

Grammar

- the verb *ser* (to be):

yo soy	I am
tú eres	you are
él/ella es	he/she/it is

Teaching ideas

Class discussion

The title of this topic is *¡Empecemos!* (Let's begin!) Start by asking the children if they already know some words or expressions in Spanish and if they know any Spanish words commonly used in English: for example, *fiesta* (party), *siesta* (afternoon nap), *loco* (crazy). Bring in real-life visual aids to promote discussion of what the children already know about Spain (for example, labels, tickets, advertisements and postcards; photos of Spanish foods such as *paella*, different *tapas*, almond cake, sweets, oranges; photos of famous people such as King Juan Carlos and Queen Sofía, sports personalities like Real Madrid's Raúl González, pop stars like Enrique Iglesias, etc.).

Answering the register

Call out names on the class register and prompt each child to respond to his or her name with *presente* (present). If a child is absent, prompt the class to respond by saying *ausente* (absent) or *falta* (missing). To end the daily roll call, teach this rhyme:

¿Quién está ausente hoy?
Name está ausente, pero no de nuestra mente (if one child is absent)
Name, name, name están ausentes, pero no de nuestra mente (if more than one child is absent)
Nadie está ausente, toda la clase está presente (if no one is absent)

Vocabulary note

Always introduce new vocabulary with either the definite article (*el/la, los/las*) or the indefinite article (*un/una*). This helps the children to remember the gender of words. Drills are a good way of practising gender: for example, say *teléfono* and prompt the children to add the correct article and a colour adjective in the correct form: *el teléfono negro*.

Spanish culture

Discuss with the children why full Spanish names are usually longer than English names. Explain that Spanish names usually include a given name, a second name, the father's surname and the mother's surname: for example, *Raquel Estela Ruíz Delgado*. Point out that many Spaniards are named after Catholic saints and the names of the Christian holy family Joseph, Mary and Jesus often feature in both girls' and boys' names: for example, María Jesús, María José, José María, Jesús María.

Mention to the children that in Spain it is common for people to greet one another with a kiss on both cheeks even if they do not know each other very well.

Notes on the activities

Page 11 ¡Hola! Introduce the lesson by saying that the children are going to find out how to answer the question *¿Cómo te llamas?* Greet the children by introducing yourself as in the activity and shaking hands. Encourage them to respond with the same expression. Once they have completed the sheet, they can create name badges with the Spanish equivalent of their own name if known, or they can choose a different Spanish name. You can find popular Spanish boys' and girls' names by searching under 'Spanish names' on the Internet. The children can act out the dialogues using their Spanish names. They could also include their surname (*el apellido*). This activity involves speaking about oneself (*yo*) and directly to someone else (*tú*). Depending on the children's ability, refer to the illustrations in ***Y ahora*** and ask *¿Cómo se llama el chico/la chica?* Encourage the children to answer with the third person: *El chico/La chica se llama José/Sandra*.

Page 12 ¡Buenos días! Introduce the greetings *Buenos días*, *Buenas tardes*, *Buenas noches* (which is used to express both 'Good evening' and 'Good night') by using drawings, flashcards (sun, moon...) or a clock. To demonstrate the difference between the informal *¿Cómo estás?* and the formal *¿Cómo está?* invite four children to come up to the front and stand in a line facing the class. Stick a post-it note on each child with one of the following names: *Carlos*, *profesora*, *Señor González*, *papá*. Model the phrases *¿Cómo estás?/¿Cómo está?* according to the person you are speaking to. Draw out that the informal *¿Cómo estás?* is used with close family and friends and that *¿Cómo está?* is a polite form of address to be used with older people, people in authority or people you don't know well. Prompt the response *Muy bien, gracias*. Invite the children to repeat the dialogue with a different set of classmates and names. After the children have completed the sheet, write up some alternative responses to the question *¿Cómo está/s?*: *Más o menos* (Not very well); *Estoy mal* (I'm feeling ill).

Page 13 ¿Quién eres tú? Enlarge the page to A3 and display. Practise the vocabulary *niño/a*, *chico/a*, *hombre/mujer* with the help of the illustrations. Ask the children *¿Quién eres tú?* and prompt them to answer appropriately. Point out that the indefinite article *un/una* is not needed in the idiomatic phrases on this page. For further practice call out *¡Niñas!* and prompt all the girls to stand up and say *¡Presente, profesor/a!* Repeat with *¡Niños!* If the class is all one gender, assign a role to each child (you could cut out and distribute the illustrations on the sheet). The children respond in role. After completing the sheet the children could create a word bank listing *niño*, *niña*, *chico*, *chica*, *hombre*, *mujer* as a reminder.

Page 14 Los colores Introduce the colours in their masculine singular form. Practise the colours by using felt-tip pens or crayons, or by pointing to classroom objects of different colours. Once the children have finished the sheet and are familiar with the colours, point out that colour adjectives always come after the noun and must agree with the noun in gender and number. As a further extension, the children could create a colour palette with the names of the colours in Spanish for a classroom display. Link this sheet with art lessons: use the activity as a starting point to discuss some Spanish works of art. Ask the children if the name on the brushes pot reminds them of anyone (Pablo Picasso). Show the children photos of Picasso's paintings and ask them to identify different colours: *¿Qué colores hay en este cuadro?* (What colours are there in this picture?)

Page 15 Los números Practise the words for the numbers 0–10 by using fingers, interlocking cubes, classroom objects, buttons, etc. Encourage the children to recite the numbers in order (*en orden*), backwards (*para atrás*) and randomly. Extend to saying only the even numbers (*los números pares*) and then only the odd numbers (*los números impares*). For safety reasons, ensure that the children use fictitious mobile phone numbers for the extension activity. The Spanish words for mobile phone are *teléfono móvil* or *celular*. As a further extension call out a number and invite the children to show the corresponding flashcard. Follow up this number practice by introducing some regular plurals of nouns. Tell the children that as a rule Spanish nouns ending in a vowel add *s* (*el número – los números*) and nouns ending in a consonant add *es* (*el color – los colores*) to form the plural. The children could learn the song *Diez pajaritos* (Ten little birds), sung to the tune of *Ten Little Indians*:

Uno, dos, tres pajaritos,
cuatro, cinco, seis pajaritos
siete, ocho, nueve pajaritos
diez pajaritos
vuelan (the children flap their arms like wings)

They could also memorise this adaptation of a traditional tongue-twister (*trabalenguas*):

Tres tristes tigres
comen trigo en un trigal.
Uno, dos, tres tristes tigres.
(Three sad tigers eat wheat in a wheat field.
One, two, three sad tigers.)

¡Hola!

Mira la lista.

Escoge las palabras.

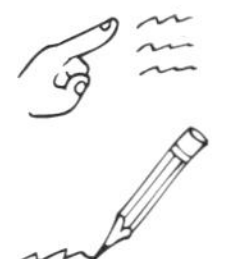

Completa las frases.

Lista

Adiós	llamo
Hasta luego	Yo me llamo
Hola	

¡Hola! Yo me ________
Marta, ¿y tú?

¡_______! ____ ____ ________
Carlos.

¡_______ _______, Marta!

¡_______, Carlos!

Escribe un diálogo.

Y ahora

Sandra

____
____
____

José

____
____
____

Translation: *Hello! Look at the list. Choose the words. Complete the sentences. • Write a dialogue.*
Teachers' note: This activity provides practice in some basic forms of greeting. Each line in the speech bubbles represents a word. Children who tackle the extension activity should write a brief dialogue modelled on one of those in the main part of the page.

¡Buenos días!

Mira la lista.
Completa las frases.
Lista
Buenos días
Buenas noches
Buenas noches
Buenas tardes
__________ __________, Carlos. ¿Cómo estás?
Bien, gracias.
__________ __________, profesora. ¿Cómo está?
Muy bien, gracias.
20:00
28°C
__________ __________, Señor González. ¿Cómo está?
Bien, gracias.
__________ __________, papá.
Buenas noches, Marta.
Y ahora
Dibuja.
¡Buenos días!
¡Buenos días!

Translation: ***Good morning!*** *Look at the list. Complete the sentences. • Draw.*
Teachers' note: In this activity the children practise different forms of greeting according to the time of day. Point out that *Buenas noches* can mean both 'Good evening' and 'Good night' depending on the circumstances. In the extension activity the children should complete the picture by showing what time of day it is through the window and add the two speakers under the speech bubbles.

¿Quién eres tú?

Escoge la frase correcta. 

Yo soy niño. ☐
Yo soy niña. ☐
Yo soy mujer. ☐

Yo soy hombre. ☐
Yo soy chica. ☐
Yo soy niño. ☐

Yo soy niña. ☐
Yo soy chica. ☐
Yo soy hombre. ☐

Yo soy niño. ☐
Yo soy mujer. ☐
Yo soy chico. ☐

Yo soy niño. ☐
Yo soy chica. ☐
Yo soy mujer. ☐

Yo soy hombre. ☐
Yo soy chica. ☐
Yo soy niño. ☐

¿Quién eres tú?
Dibuja.
Escribe.

Translation: ***Who are you?*** *Choose the correct sentence.* • *Who are you? Draw. Write.*
Teachers' note: This sheet offers an opportunity for practising reading comprehension in Spanish. It presents the *yo* (I) and *tú* (you) forms of the verb *ser* (to be). The activity also provides vocabulary relating to gender and age group with which the children can identify. As an extension the children should draw themselves on a blank piece of paper and write a short sentence describing themselves based on the model in the main activity.

Los colores

Colorea el papagayo.

diccionario

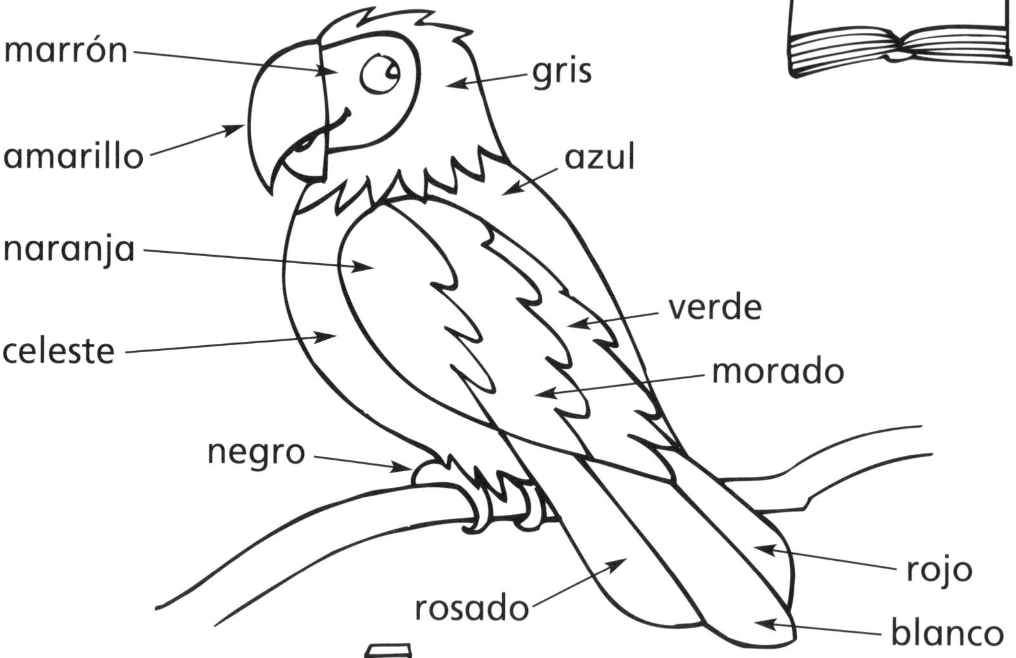

marrón
amarillo
naranja
celeste
negro
gris
azul
verde
morado
rosado
rojo
blanco

Y ahora

Busca los colores en la sopa de letras.

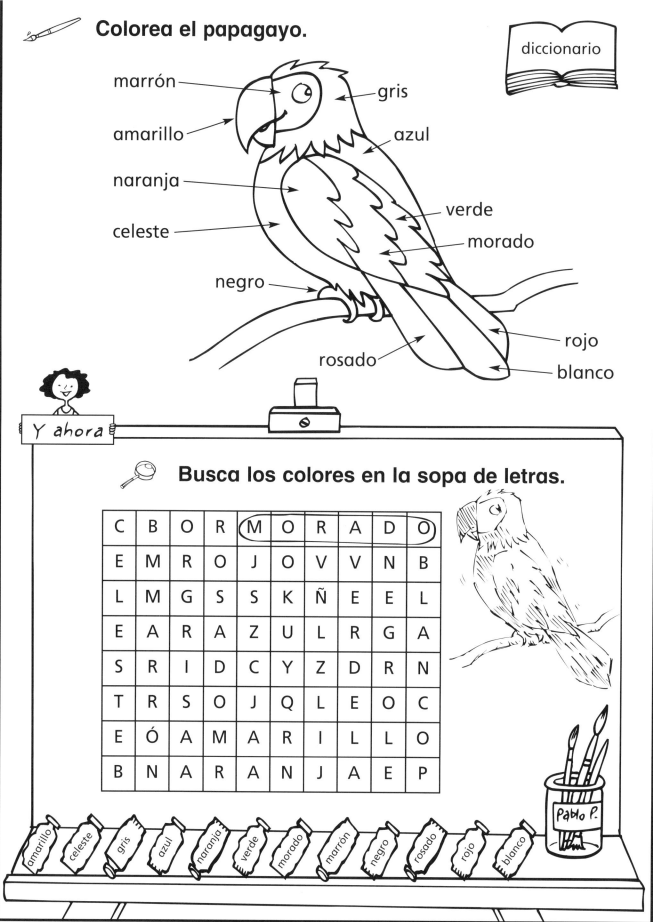

C	B	O	R	M	O	R	A	D	O
E	M	R	O	J	O	V	V	N	B
L	M	G	S	S	K	Ñ	E	E	L
E	A	R	A	Z	U	L	R	G	A
S	R	I	D	C	Y	Z	D	R	N
T	R	S	O	J	Q	L	E	O	C
E	Ó	A	M	A	R	I	L	L	O
B	N	A	R	A	N	J	A	E	P

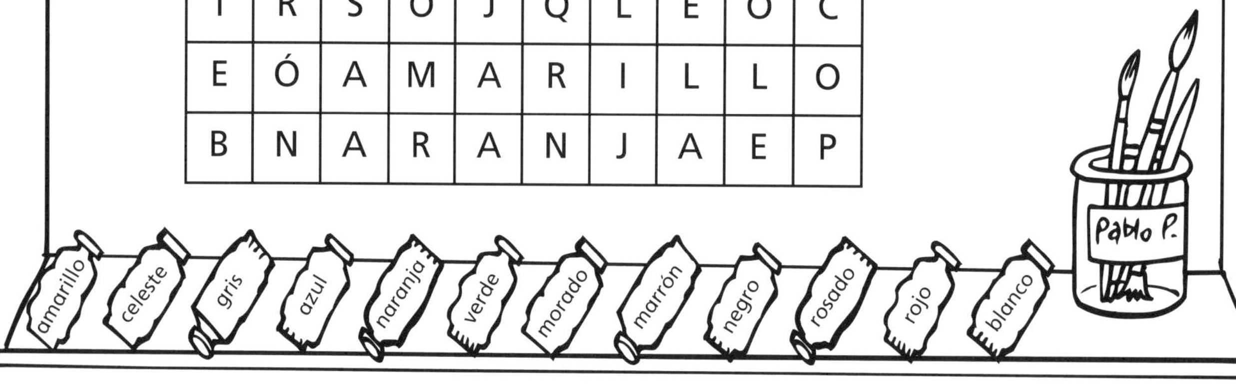

amarillo, celeste, gris, azul, naranja, verde, morado, marrón, negro, rosado, rojo, blanco

Pablo P.

Translation: *Colours. Colour the parrot. • Find the colours in the wordsearch.*
Teachers' note: On this sheet the children learn the Spanish names for colours, recognise their written form and match the name to the colour in a practical colouring activity. They should use a dictionary to find any colours they do not know. It may be helpful to enlarge the page for those children who tackle the extension activity.

Los números

Escribe el número.

Corta las fichas.

	0 cero
uno	dos
tres	cuatro
cinco	seis
siete	ocho
nueve	diez

Y ahora

Practica el diálogo.

¿Cuál es tu número de teléfono?

Mi número es ________________.

Marta

Carlos

Teachers' note: Enlarge the page to A3 and copy it onto card. This sheet offers a variety of opportunities for using the numbers 0–10 (see **Notes on the activities**, page 10). The children could work in pairs to quiz each other, covering either the digit(s) or the word. For the extension activity the children should work in pairs, taking turns to invent phone numbers and saying the numbers one digit at a time.

Topic 2: La escuela

Key vocabulary

la escuela	school
un alumno/a	pupil
un bolígrafo	ballpoint pen
una clase	class/classroom
un cuaderno	exercise book
un diccionario	dictionary
un estuche	pencil case
una goma	rubber
un lápiz	pencil
un libro	book
una mesa	table
una mochila	rucksack
un ordenador	computer
el papel	paper
una hoja de papel	sheet of paper
el pegamento	glue
un profesor/una profesora	teacher
un registro	register
una regla	ruler
un reloj	clock
un rotulador	felt-tip pen
un sacapuntas	pencil sharpener
una silla	chair
unas tijeras	scissors
las asignaturas	school subjects
la educación física	PE
el español	Spanish
la geografía	Geography
la historia	History
la informática	ICT
el inglés	English
las matemáticas	Maths
la música	Music
aburrido/a	boring
difícil	difficult
divertido/a	fun
fácil	easy
aquí	here

Expressions

¿Cuántos/as hay?	How many are there?
¿Dónde está...?	Where is...?
¿Qué es?	What is it?
¡Abrid!	Open!
¡Cerrad!	Close!
¡Escuchad!	Listen!
¡Levantaos!	Stand up!
¡Mirad!	Look!
¡Repetid!	Repeat!
¡Sentaos!	Sit down!
¡Silencio!	Be quiet!
¿Cómo es...?	What's ... like?
¿Puedo ir a beber agua, por favor?	May I go and get a drink of water, please?
¿Puedo ir al baño, por favor?	May I go to the toilet, please?
Lo siento.	I'm sorry.
No entiendo.	I don't understand.
No sé.	I don't know.
Perdón	Excuse me
por favor	please

Grammar

- *hay/no hay* — there is, there are/ there isn't, there aren't
- the verb *tener* (to have):

yo tengo	I have
tú tienes	you have (sing. inform.)
usted tiene	you have (sing. form.)
él/ella tiene	he/she has

- prepositions of place: *en* (in), *sobre* (on), *debajo de* (under)

Teaching ideas

Classroom routine

To promote the speaking of Spanish as much as possible, use this simple rhyme when children lapse into English: *Uno, dos, tres, no se habla en inglés.*

Picture dictionary

Use the Picture dictionary on pages 26 and 27 to revise classroom vocabulary. Ask questions such as *¿Hay una bandera en la clase?* (Is there a flag in the classroom?) or *¿Dónde está la papelera?* (Where is the bin?) or say *Colorea las dos mochilas de amarillo* (Colour the two schoolbags yellow). Ask the children to mime the action verbs that they can see in the Picture dictionary. You could mask the dictionary around the border for quizzes and tests.

Spanish culture

Topic 2 uses the generic, international term *escuela* for school. The word *colegio* as featured on the pull-out frieze is the term commonly used by primary school children in Spain, who say they go to *el cole*.

Notes on the activities

Page 18 En la mochila Introduce the names of classroom objects with real examples or make a set of flashcards by enlarging the activity sheet to A3. Place the flashcards or objects in a school rucksack and pull them out one by one. Once the children have grasped how to pronouce the name of the object and know its gender, draw out a card or object and ask *¿Qué es?* Prompt the children to answer with a complete sentence: *Es un/una…* Encourage them to repeat this activity with their partner. They could make additional flashcards of classroom objects with the help of a dictionary. For further practice, play *Voy a Madrid y llevo…*, as described on pages 6–7. The children could make large labels for classroom objects to display around the room.

Page 19 ¿Cuántos hay? Review numbers and the names of classroom objects with the children. Place a few classroom objects in a school rucksack. Invite the children to take out the objects and to answer questions such as *¿Cuántos lápices hay en la mochila?* or *¿Cuántas reglas hay en la mochila?* As a further extension introduce the negative form *No hay*. Using the picture on the activity sheet, ask a question about something that is not shown: for example, *¿Cuántos relojes hay en la clase?* and prompt the answer: *No hay (ningún) reloj en la clase* (There aren't any clocks in the classroom). Or say *¿Hay una profesora en la clase?* to elicit the answer *No, no hay (ninguna) profesora en la clase* (No, there isn't a female teacher in the classroom).

Page 20 Yo tengo… To introduce the first, second and third persons singular of the verb *tener* (to have) use classroom objects and mime. For example, hold up a ballpoint pen and say *Yo tengo un bolígrafo*. Repeat using *Tú tienes*, *Él tiene*, *Ella tiene* and *Usted tiene*. Prompt the children to repeat the sentences. Explain that *usted* is a polite form of address. To extend the activity encourage the children to make negative sentences by placing *no* in front of the conjugated verb: for example, *Yo no tengo una regla*.

Page 21 ¿Dónde está…? Introduce the prepositions of place *en*, *sobre* and *debajo de* by placing a classroom object in, on or under a container (a pencil case, a rucksack, an envelope or a box): for example, place a rubber in a pencil case and say *La goma está en el estuche*. Then ask *¿Dónde está la goma?* Encourage the children to answer using the same sentence. Pairs of children could use the Picture dictionary on pages 26 and 27 to ask and answer questions about the location of objects. The class could also play a game of *¿Dónde está?* Ask a volunteer to cover his or her eyes. Hide a classroom object in, on or under something else. The volunteer should look for the object and say where it is. The other children help by saying *frío* (cold) when he or she is far away from the object, *tibio* (lukewarm) when he or she is near the object and *caliente* (hot) when he or she is right by it.

Page 22 ¡Escuchad! To introduce the commands presented in the activity make a set of enlarged flashcards, hold them up and mime them for the class. Then mix up the cards and place them face down on a table. Invite a child to come up, take a card and read the command aloud. The class must obey (or mime) the command. Repeat with other volunteers. For extra practice, without the aid of the flashcards, play *Simón dice* (Simon says).

Page 23 ¡En español, por favor! Encourage the children to become familiar with and use typical Spanish expressions. When they forget to use a phrase they know, say *¡En español, por favor!* As a further extension activity the children could create a poster of useful expressions to be displayed in class. Include other words or phrases you might use in class such as *Gracias* (Thank you) and *De nada* (Not at all).

Page 24 Las asignaturas Ask the children to work in groups. Give each group an enlarged copy of their own lesson timetable. Distribute sets of post-it notes with the Spanish names of the eight school subjects listed on the sheet. Ask each group to replace the English lesson names on their timetable with their Spanish equivalents. Encourage the children to look up in a dictionary the words for other school subjects they might have and add them to the timetable: for example, art, drama, DT. Discuss any similarities between the Spanish and the English word. Point out that the names of school subjects are not written with an initial capital letter in Spanish. Link this sheet with literacy, music and history. Explain that the book *Don Quijote* was written 400 years ago by Spain's most famous writer Miguel de Cervantes and is widely regarded as the first modern novel. See http://spanishbooks.netfirms.com/quijote.htm for a short synopsis. Mention also that the guitar is the most typical Spanish musical instrument and is used to accompany *flamenco* dancing, particularly in the south of Spain. Relate the history illustration to Christopher Columbus, who sailed from Spain to America in 1492.

Page 25 El español es fácil Use facial expressions and mime to introduce the four adjectives *fácil*, *difícil*, *divertido/a* and *aburrido/a*. With the help of the Spanish timetable made during work on page 24, ask the children *¿Cómo es la clase de informática?* Encourage them to express their opinion by saying *Es divertida/Es aburrida* and using a thumbs up/thumbs down gesture. Note that a Spanish adjective agrees in gender (masculine/feminine) and number (singular/plural) with the noun it describes.

En la mochila

Mira la lista.

Escoge las palabras.

Escribe las palabras.

Corta las fichas.

Lista

un bolígrafo	un libro
un cuaderno	el papel
un estuche	el pegamento
una goma	una regla
un lápiz	un sacapuntas

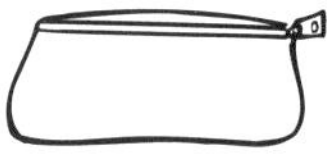

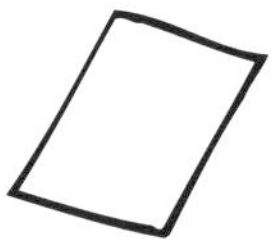

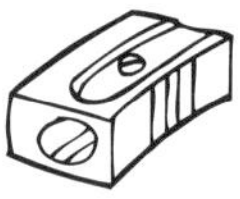

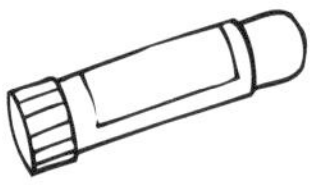

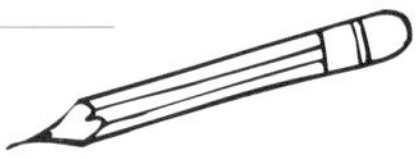

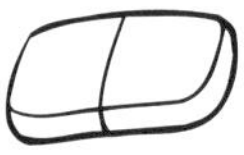

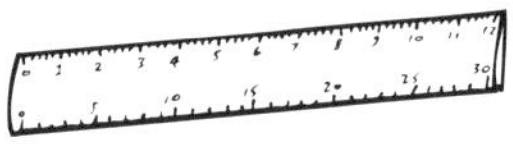

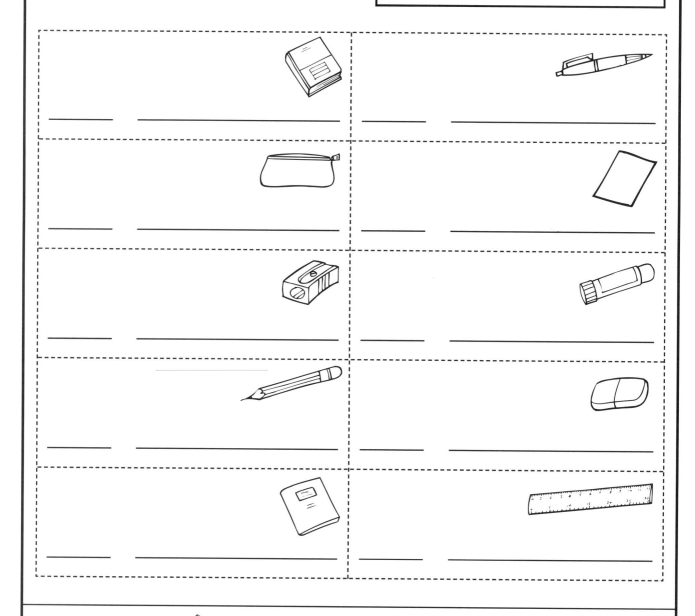

Escribe las palabras en inglés detrás de las fichas.

Translation: ***In the school rucksack.*** *Look at the list. Choose the words. Write the words. Cut out the cards.*
• *Write the words in English on the back of the cards.*
Teachers' note: Enlarge the page to A3 and copy it onto card. This sheet helps the children to name some common classroom objects. The article should be written on the short solid line and the noun on the long solid line. Point out the difference between the masculine indefinite article *un* and the feminine indefinite article *una*.

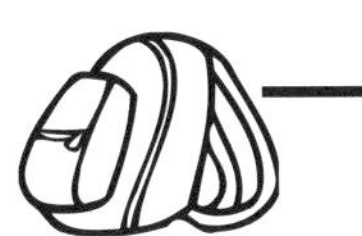

¿Cuántos hay?

Mira el dibujo.

Cuenta.

Escribe.

Hay un profesor. ____ ________ estuches.

Hay dos mochilas. ____ ________ reglas.

____ ________ mesas. ____ ________ libros.

Practica el diálogo.

Y ahora
¿Cuántos libros hay aquí?
Hay ocho libros.

Translation: *How many are there? Look at the picture. Count. Write.* • *Practise the dialogue.*

Teachers' note: This activity practises the invariable verb form *Hay* (There is/There are) and numbers up to 10. It also introduces the question word *¿Cuántos/as?* (How many?) Point out the difference between *¿Cuántos libros hay?* (masculine) and *¿Cuántas mesas hay?* (feminine). In the extension activity the children should practise the dialogue in pairs and then talk about people and objects in the main picture.

Yo tengo...

Mira la lista.

Escoge la palabra.

Completa las frases.

Lista

tengo
tiene
tiene
tienes

Yo __________ cuatro registros.

Tú __________ tres bolígrafos.

Usted __________ dos cuadernos.

¿Qué tienes en tu mochila?

Escribe una frase.

Translation: ***I have...*** *Look at the list. Choose the word. Complete the sentences. • What have you got in your rucksack? Write a sentence.*

Teachers' note: This activity gives practice in using the first, second and third persons singular of the verb *tener* (to have). For the extension activity the children should write about the contents of their own rucksack, paying careful attention to the spelling of numbers and the plural form of nouns.

¿Dónde está...?

 **Mira la lista.**

 **Lee las frases.**

 **Completa las frases.**

Lista
debajo de
en
sobre

1 El bolígrafo está *en* el estuche.

2 El diccionario está *sobre* la mesa.

3 La mochila está *debajo de* la silla.

4 La goma está __________ la mesa.

5 El sacapuntas está __________ el ordenador.

6 La regla está __________ la mochila.

 **Dibuja un libro sobre la silla.**

 **Dibuja una hoja de papel en la papelera.**

Dibuja unas tijeras debajo de la mesa.

Translation: ***Where is...?*** *Look at the list. Read the sentences. Complete the sentences. • Draw a book on the chair. Draw a sheet of paper in the bin. Draw scissors under the table.*
Teachers' note: This activity gives practice in indicating where an object is located using the prepositions of place *en* (in), *sobre* (on) and *debajo de* (under) when answering the question *¿Dónde está...?* (Where is...?) In the extension activity the children should draw the items in the correct position on the main picture.

¡Escuchad!

 **Corta las palabras.**

 **Pega las palabras debajo de los dibujos.**

 **Corta las fichas.**

 **Practica con tu compañero/a.**

¡Mirad!	¡Escuchad!	¡Repetid!	¡Abrid!
¡Cerrad!	¡Sentaos!	¡Levantaos!	¡Silencio!

Translation: ***Listen!*** *Cut out the words. Glue the words under the pictures. Cut out the cards. Practise with your partner.*

Teachers' note: Copy the sheet onto A3 card. This activity helps the children to learn classroom instructions. Ask them to match the labels to the pictures. They should use one set of cards between two, placed face-down. One child picks up a card and mimes the command. His or her partner obeys it, then picks up the next card and so on.

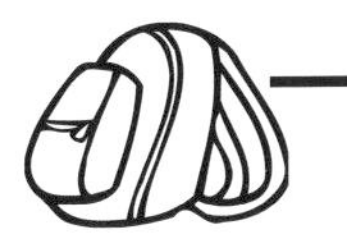

¡En español, por favor!

 **Mira los dibujos.**

 **Mira la lista.**

 **Completa las frases.**

Lista

Lo siento
No entiendo
No sé
Perdón
¿Puedo ir al baño, por favor?
¿Puedo ir a beber agua, por favor?

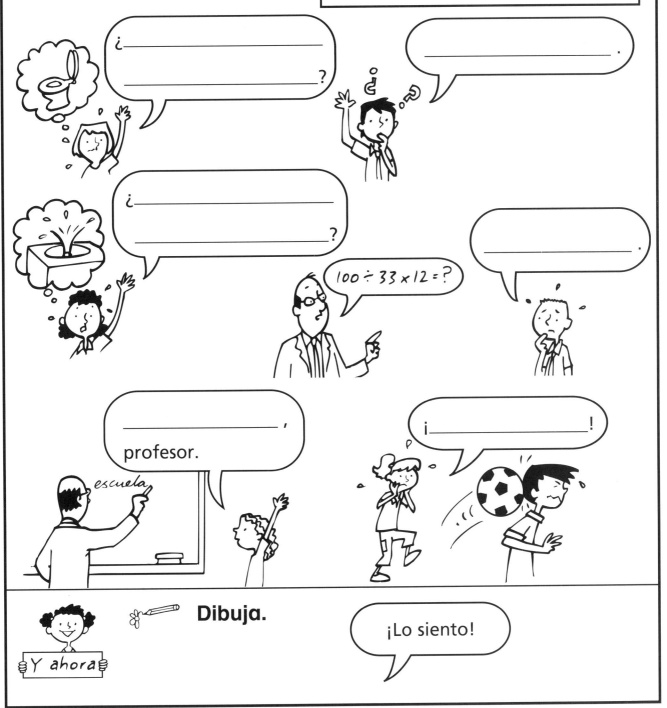

¿______________________________
______________________________?

______________________________.

¿______________________________
______________________________?

100 ÷ 33 x 12 = ?

______________________________.

______________________________,
profesor.

escuela

¡______________________________!

Y ahora

Dibuja.

¡Lo siento!

Translation: ***In Spanish, please!*** *Look at the pictures. Look at the list. Complete the sentences. • Draw.*
Teachers' note: This activity encourages the children to use Spanish when making a request, answering questions and excusing themselves from class. To help them with the pronunciation, read the sentences together. For the extension activity ask the children to draw an appropriate scene on a separate piece of paper to match the expression in the speech bubble.

Las asignaturas

Mira los dibujos y las palabras.

Une con una línea el dibujo y la palabra.

• español •

• matemáticas •

• historia •

• inglés •

• música •

• informática •

• educación física •

• geografía •

Escribe las palabras.

Busca la palabra escondida.

 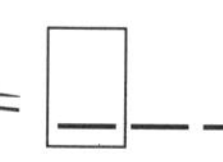  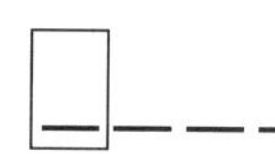 

  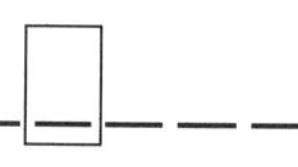

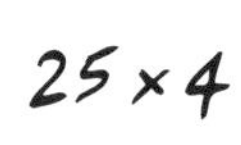

 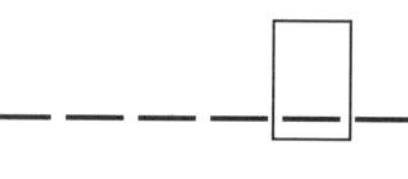

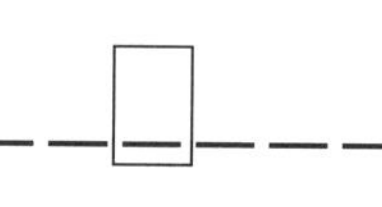

¡  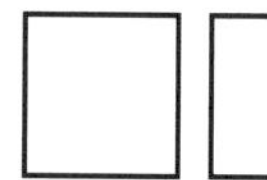 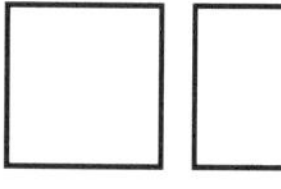 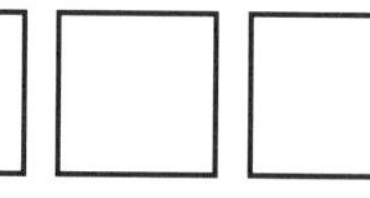 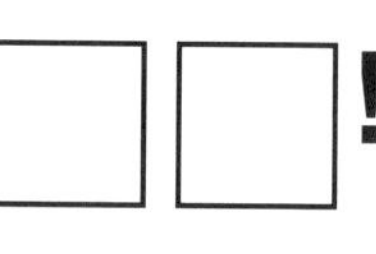 !

Translation: ***School subjects****. Look at the pictures and the words. Draw a line to join the drawing and the word. • Write the words. Find the hidden word.*

Teachers' note: This activity helps the children to practise the names of school subjects and to become familiar with their written form. In the extension activity they must rearrange the boxed letters to find the hidden word, which means the same as the words on the rosette.

El español es fácil

Lee las palabras.

Completa las frases.

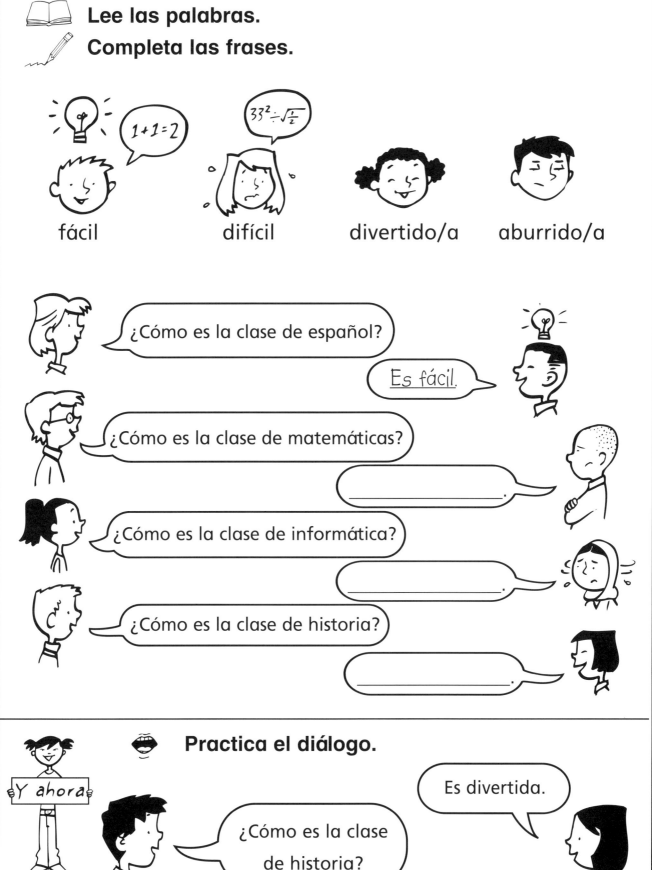

fácil difícil divertido/a aburrido/a

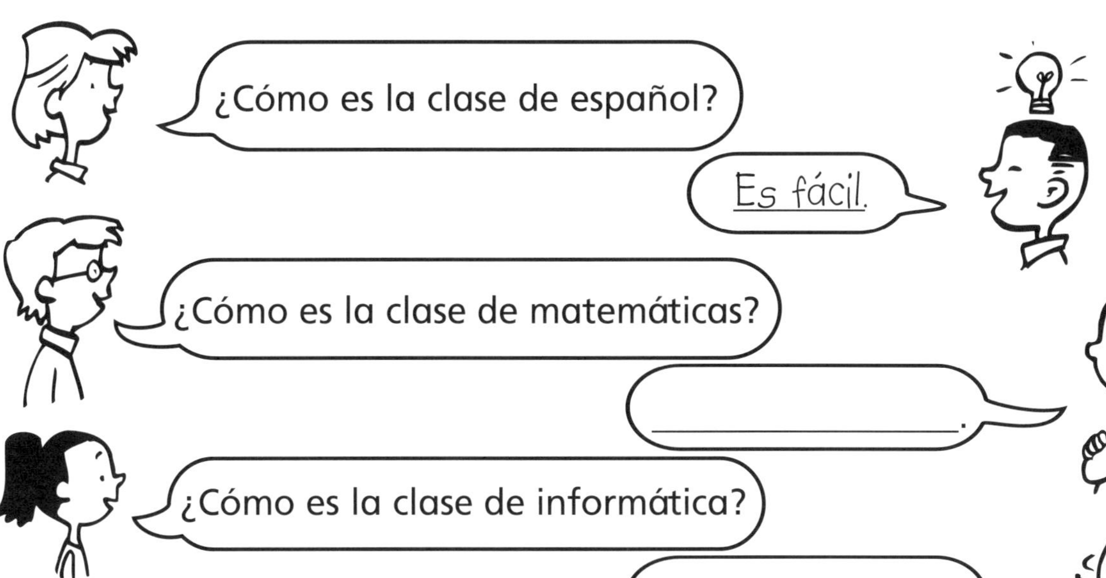

¿Cómo es la clase de español?

Es fácil.

¿Cómo es la clase de matemáticas?

____________________.

¿Cómo es la clase de informática?

____________________.

¿Cómo es la clase de historia?

____________________.

Practica el diálogo.

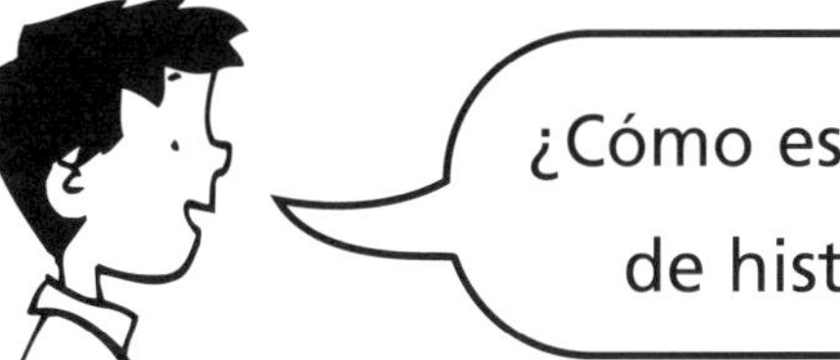

¿Cómo es la clase de historia?

Es divertida.

Translation: *Spanish is easy. Read the words. Complete the sentences. • Practise the dialogue.*
Teachers' note: This activity revises school subjects and introduces four adjectives and the question word *¿Cómo?* (What? or How?) In the extension activity the children should practise the dialogue in pairs and then change the school subject and their view of it to encourage independent thought. All the answers in this activity must agree with the feminine noun *la clase. Fácil* and *difícil* are invariable in the singular.

Picture dictionary

¡Todos en clase!

Deberes
ESPAÑOL
DICCIONARIO
contar
escribir
leer
el pupitre
el ordenador
las pinturas
el papel
el diccionario
la pizarra
la tiza
el mapa

Topic 3: La familia

Key vocabulary

la familia	family
la abuela	grandmother
el abuelo	grandfather
el bebé	baby
los/las gemelos/as	twins
la hermana	sister
la hermanastra	stepsister
el hermano	brother
el hermanastro	stepbrother
la hija	daughter
el hijo	son
la madre	mother
la madrastra	stepmother
la nieta	granddaughter
el nieto	grandson
el padre	father
el padrastro	stepfather
la prima	cousin (female)
el primo	cousin (male)
la tía	aunt
el tío	uncle
la foto	photo
alto/a	tall
antipático/a	unfriendly
bajo/a	short
joven	young
simpático/a	nice/fun
viejo/a	old

Expressions

¿Cuántos hermanos tienes?	How many brothers and sisters have you got?
¿Cómo es ...?	What is ... like?
¿Cómo eres tú?	What are you like?
Ésta es mi familia.	This is my family.
Mi ... se llama...	My ...'s name is...
Yo soy hijo/a único/a.	I am an only child.

Grammar

- masculine and feminine forms of nouns and adjectives: *hermano/hermana, abuelo/abuela; alto/alta, viejo/vieja*
- possessive adjective *mi* (my)

Teaching ideas

Vocabulary note

To introduce the names of family members bring in a picture of a real family. You could use a picture of the Spanish royal family. Due to the sensitivity of the topic, remember to include different types of families. Some children might need to know words such as *padrastro, madrastra, hermanastro, hermanastra*.

Picture dictionary

Use the Picture dictionary on pages 38 and 39 to revise family vocabulary. Ask questions starting with *¿Quién?*: for example, *¿Quién saca fotos?* (Who is taking photos?) and *¿Quién es alto?* (Who is tall?) or other questions such as *¿Cuántas personas hay?* (How many people are there?) and *¿Es una familia grande o pequeña?* (Is it a large or a small family?) If the children are ready, point out that the verbs in squares around the Picture dictionary all end in *-ar*. Use this as an introduction to the present tense conjugation of regular *-ar* verbs:

yo bailo	I dance
tú bailas	you dance (sing. inform.)
usted baila	you dance (sing. form.)
él/ella baila	he/she dances
nosotros/as bailamos	we dance
vosotros/as bailáis	you dance (pl. inform.)
ustedes bailan	you dance (pl. form.)
ellos/as bailan	they dance

This Picture dictionary depicts a birthday party. Teach the birthday song in Spanish (it is sung to the same tune as *Happy birthday* in English):

Cumpleaños feliz,
cumpleaños feliz.
Te deseamos todos
Cumpleaños feliz.

Spanish culture

Taking your cue from the Picture dictionary, discuss with children how, in Spain, grandparents and extended family members very often live together or close to each other. Ask children to share how often and on what occasions they see their own extended family. Sensitivity to some children's personal circumstances may be required.

Notes on the activities

Page 30 Mi familia Draw a family on the board or display a picture of a large family. Give each family member a name. Pointing to each one, introduce the family members with sentences such as *Ernesto es mi abuelo* (Ernesto is my grandfather), *Pilar es mi madre* (Pilar is my mother). Stress the possessive adjective *mi* with your voice. When the children are confident with this construction, present the family again, this time saying *Mi abuelo se llama Ernesto* (My grandfather's name is Ernesto), *Mi madre se llama Pilar* (My mother's name is Pilar). As a further extension to the activity sheet prompt the children to answer specific questions such as *¿Cómo se llama tu hermano?* (What's your brother's name?)

Page 31 La familia de Carlos To introduce the activity sheet, enlarge Carlos's family tree. You could give the picture the title *Árbol genealógico de la familia de Carlos*. Use it to review the words for family members. Ask those children who have completed the extension activity to write a corrected version of the false sentence. The children could create their own family tree to display in class. Remember to be sensitive to special family situations. Alternatively, they could make up a family tree of a famous cartoon or TV character.

Page 32 ¿Cuántos hermanos tienes? Review the *yo*, *tú*, *él*, *ella* and *usted* forms of the verb *tener* (see page 16). Ask each child *¿Cuántos hermanos tienes?* and prompt the correct reply. Point out that although the question uses the masculine plural form *hermanos*, it refers to both brothers and sisters. Children who do not have any brothers or sisters can reply with *Yo soy hijo/a único/a*. *Yo soy hijo único* is the masculine form of 'I am an only child' and *Yo soy hija única* is the feminine form. Make sure that the children grasp the ideas of gender and adjectival agreement.

Page 33 Foto de familia Use this sheet to review the words for family members including extended family members *tío* (uncle), *tía* (aunt), *primo* (male cousin), *prima* (female cousin). Give groups of children photographs of different families cut from magazines or clothes catalogues and ask them to take turns to identify who each family member is. Some may also be able to give each person a name and an age. As a further extension activity, you could write up the words for all the male family members and ask volunteers to say the female equivalent: for example, *tío/*__ (*tía*). Some children may ask for the words for nephew and niece: *sobrino/sobrina*.

Page 34 Dominó de adjetivos Enlarge the dominoes on the activity sheet to make cards to use with the whole class. Make sure that each image is clearly visible. To introduce the adjectives hold up a card and say *Este hombre es alto* (This man is tall) or *Esta mujer es alta* (This woman is tall). You could also ask *¿Cómo es este hombre?* (What is this man like?) or *¿Cómo es esta mujer?* (What is this woman like?) and prompt the correct response: *(El hombre) es alto* or *(La mujer) es alta*. As an extension activity the children could make extra domino cards with adjectives such as *guapo/guapa* (good-looking), *feo/fea* (ugly). Suggest that for these they could draw a beautiful heroine and an ugly beast or a good-looking hero and an ugly witch.

Page 35 ¿Cómo es? Display the enlarged cards from page 34 to review the adjectives the children have learned. Show pictures of people cut out of magazines and ask questions about their physical appearance, using the phrase *¿Cómo es?* Make sure the children use the correct form of each adjective in their answers, according to whether the person described is male or female. As a further extension activity, they could write a sentence describing themselves, a friend or a TV personality.

Page 36 ¡Pon en orden! Discuss with the children the structure of a typical Spanish sentence, focusing especially on the personal pronoun as the subject of the sentence. Point out that both *Yo soy bajo* and *Soy bajo* are grammatically correct. As an extension activity ask the children to add brackets around the part of the sentence that could be omitted without changing the meaning or making it incorrect. Give them other sentence puzzles for more practice: for example, *¿Cómo se llama la madre de Pedro? Pedro llama madre Úrsula se La de; ¿Cuántos primos tiene tu amigo? tiene Mi tres amigo primos; ¿Cómo es el tío de Carmen? es tío El Carmen simpático de.*

Page 37 ¡Sonríe! Before the children tackle the activity sheet discuss how a bilingual dictionary is structured and look up the new words that appear in the text: *vivir*, *delgado*, *bonito*, *bigote*, *juguetón*, *juego, siempre*. Discuss how word families can help you to work out what new words mean and to remember them: for example, *juego*, *jugamos*, *juguetón*. Point out the final sentence: *José tiene cuatro años*. Explain that this is how to express age in Spanish, using the correct part of the verb *tener* (to have) followed by the number of years. Children could practise asking each other *¿Cuántos años tienes?* and responding *Tengo ... años*. After the children have completed the reading activity, show them a reproduction of Diego Velázquez's painting *Las Meninas* (Museo del Prado, Madrid) on which this illustration is modelled. Picasso also painted a version of *Las Meninas* in 1957 (Museo Picasso, Barcelona). Discuss how in the past people commissioned family portraits whereas today people take photographs.

Mi familia

Mira la lista.

Escoge las palabras.

Completa las frases.

Lista

abuela
abuelo
hermano
madre
padre

Mi hermana se llama Mariana.

Mi ____________ se llama Gustavo.

Mi ____________ se llama Lucía.

Mi ____________ se llama Ernesto.

Mi ____________ se llama Pablo.

Mi ____________ se llama Pilar.

Dibuja un miembro de tu familia.

¿Cómo se llama?

Escribe una frase.

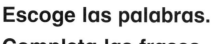

Translation: ***My family***. *Look at the list. Choose the words. Complete the sentences. • Draw a member of your family. What is his or her name? Write a sentence.*

Teachers' note: This activity sheet helps the children to practise the words for members of the family and shows how to introduce them. For the extension activity the children should write a complete sentence modelled on those in the main activity.

La familia de Carlos

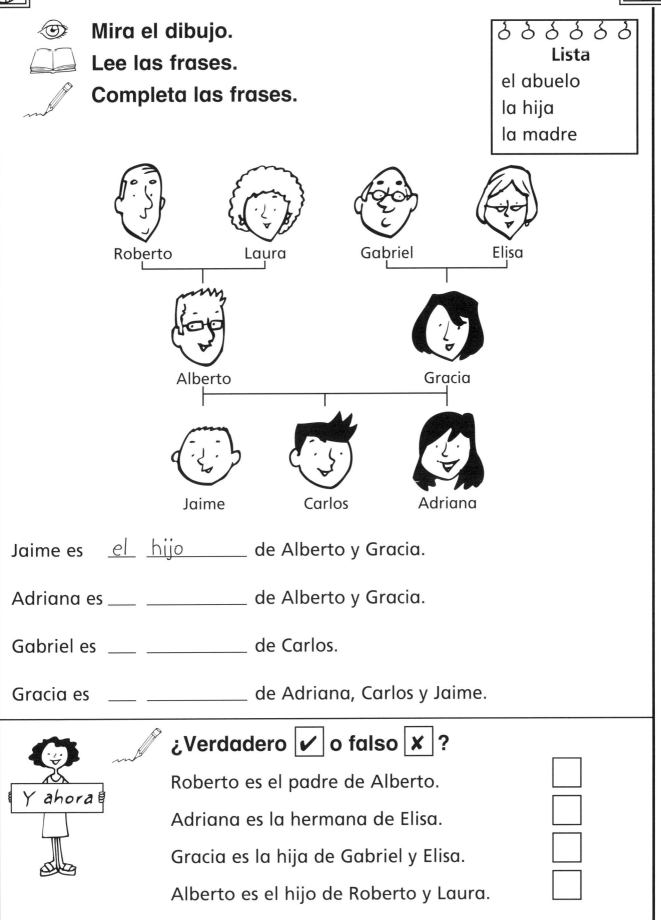

Mira el dibujo.
Lee las frases.
Completa las frases.

Lista
el abuelo
la hija
la madre

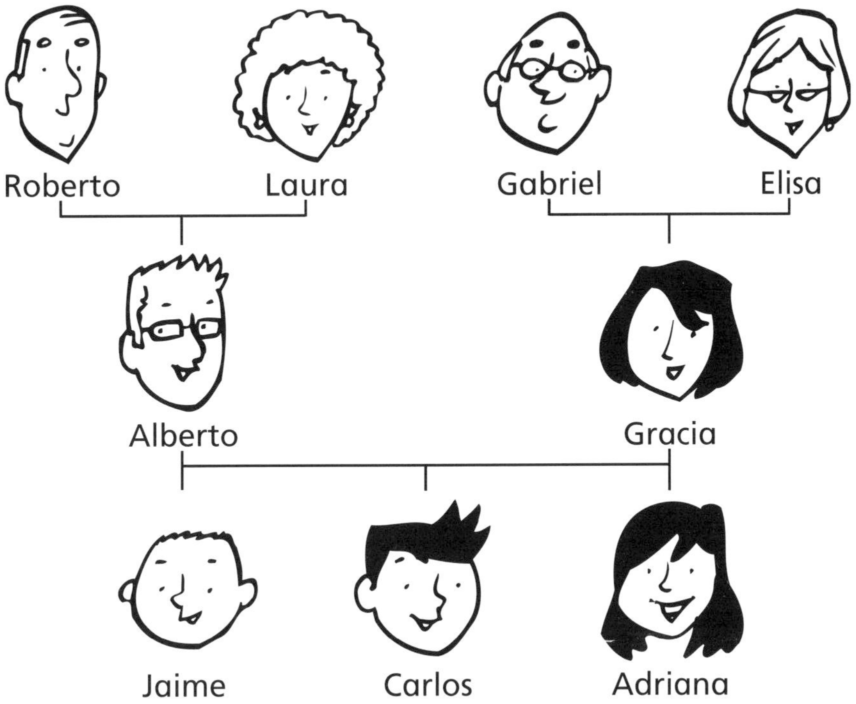

Roberto — Laura
Gabriel — Elisa
Alberto — Gracia
Jaime, Carlos, Adriana

Jaime es el hijo de Alberto y Gracia.

Adriana es ___ ___________ de Alberto y Gracia.

Gabriel es ___ ___________ de Carlos.

Gracia es ___ ___________ de Adriana, Carlos y Jaime.

¿Verdadero ✔ o falso ✘ ?

Roberto es el padre de Alberto. ☐

Adriana es la hermana de Elisa. ☐

Gracia es la hija de Gabriel y Elisa. ☐

Alberto es el hijo de Roberto y Laura. ☐

Translation: *Carlos's family. Look at the picture. Read the sentences. Complete the sentences. • True or false?*
Teachers' note: This activity reinforces the words for family members and introduces *hijo* (son) and *hija* (daughter). Discuss with the children how a family tree is set up. Once they have completed the activity they could make up new True/False sentences based on Carlos's family as a quiz for their partner.

¿Cuántos hermanos tienes?

 **Mira los dibujos.**

 **Lee las frases.**

Une con una línea el dibujo y la frase.

• Yo tengo una hermana.•

• Yo tengo dos hermanos.•

• Yo soy hija única.•

• Yo tengo dos hermanas gemelas.•

• Yo tengo un hermano y una hermana.•

• Yo tengo tres hermanos.•

• Yo soy hijo único.•

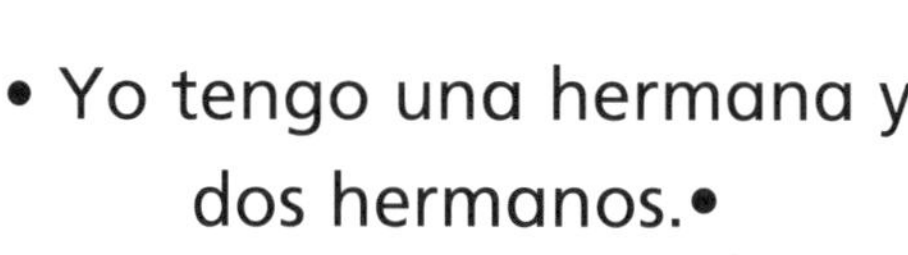

• Yo tengo una hermana y dos hermanos.•

Practica el diálogo.

¿Cuántos hermanos tienes?

Yo tengo un hermano y una hermana.

Translation: ***¿How many brothers and sisters do you have?*** *Look at the pictures. Read the sentences. Draw a line to join the pictures with the sentences. • Practise the dialogue.*
Teachers' note: In this matching activity the children should join the sentence referring to the underlined character in each picture to the correct picture box. Invite them to use the dialogue modelled in the extension activity to survey different classmates.

Foto de familia

¿Quién es?

Mira la foto y las palabras.

Completa las frases.

La madre de mi madre es mi _______________.

El hermano de mi padre es mi _______________.

El hijo de mi tía es mi _______________.

La madre de mi prima es mi _______________.

La hija de mi tío es mi _______________.

Mi hermana es la _______________ de mi abuelo.

Trabaja con un/a compañero/a.

Escribe dos frases incompletas más.

Tu compañero/a debe adivinar quién es.

Translation: ***Family photo.*** *Who is it? Look at the picture and the words. Complete the sentences.*
• *Work with a partner. Write two more incomplete sentences. Your partner must guess who it is.*
Teachers' note: This activity practises the names of family members. Go over the words to ensure correct pronunciation and understanding. For the extension activity the children should write their own sentence starters and ask a partner to work out who the family member is.

Dominó de adjetivos

Corta las fichas.

Juega dominó.

antipática		simpática	
joven		baja	
joven		alto	
alta		vieja	
antipático		viejo	
bajo		simpático	

Translation: ***Adjective dominoes.*** *Cut out the cards. Play dominoes.*

Teachers' note: This activity presents six adjectives in their masculine and feminine forms describing people. Make sure that the children understand the meaning of each adjective and to which drawing each one corresponds. Point out that *joven* (young) does not change. The children can first play individually and then with a partner, using only one set of cards.

¿Cómo es?

Mira la lista.

Escoge la palabra.

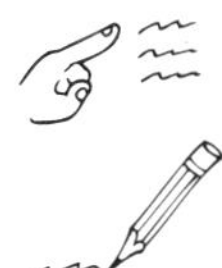

Completa las frases.

Lista	
bajo	es
joven	es
simpática	es
viejo	soy

La abuela de Carlos ______________ vieja.

El padre de Carlos ________________ alto.

El abuelo de Carlos es ________________.

Yo ______________ joven.

La hermana de Carlos es ________________.

El abuelo de Carlos es ________________.

El hermano de Carlos es ______________.

La madre de Carlos ____________ joven y alta.

¿Cómo eres tú?

Dibuja.

Habla con tu compañero/a.

Translation: ***What is he/she like?*** *Look at the list. Choose the word. Complete the sentences.*
• *What are you like? Draw. Talk to your partner.*
Teachers' note: This activity reinforces the words for family members and some adjectives describing personal characteristics. For the extension activity encourage the children to draw themselves and then to describe themselves orally.

¡Pon en orden!

Corta las palabras.

Pega las palabras en orden debajo de las preguntas.

¿Cómo se llama el padre de Gustavo?

¿Cómo es la prima de Raúl?

¿Cuántos hermanos tienes tú?

soy	único	Yo	hijo

prima	alta	es	La	Raúl	de

Él	Alfonso	se	García	llama

Translation: ***Put in order!*** *Cut out the words. Glue the words in order under the questions.*
Teachers' note: This activity revises the three expressions *¿Cómo se llama?*, *¿Cómo es?*, *¿Cuántos hermanos tienes?* and their answers. Each set of mixed-up words at the bottom of the page makes one sentence and must be glued under the appropriate question in the right order. Suggest that the children try out the word sequences orally before sticking the words down.

¡Sonríe!

 **Mira el dibujo.**

 **Lee.**

¡Hola! Yo me llamo Margarita. Vivo con mi madre, mi padre y mi perro. Mi madre se llama María. Es delgada y bonita. Mi padre se llama Felipe. Es alto y tiene bigote. Mi perro se llama Choco. Es marrón y juguetón. Yo juego con mis primos Inés, Clara y José. Clara y yo siempre jugamos a las cartas. Inés y Clara son gemelas. José tiene cuatro años.

 **¿Quién es? Escribe la letra.**

María ____ Margarita ____

José ____ Choco ____

Clara ____ Felipe ____

Inés ____

Translation: *Smile! Look at the picture. Read. Who is it? Write the letter.*
Teachers' note: This reading comprehension revisits vocabulary for how to present oneself and one's family members and includes adjectives of physical description. The children should look at the drawing and read the text, and then write the correct letter next to the name of each character. Encourage them to use a dictionary to look up any unfamiliar words.

Picture dictionary

¡Feliz

el padre

la madre

el hijo

la hija

el abuelo

la abuela

el niño

la niña

el bebé

el globo

el pastel

Fiesta de cumpleaños

cumpleaños, abuelo!

afectuoso/a

viejo/a

joven

sacar una fotografía

bailar

el regalo

el gato

el perro

abrazar

amar

besar

Topic 4: La casa

Key vocabulary

la casa	house/home
la alfombra	carpet
el armario	wardrobe
la bañera	bathtub
el baño	bathroom
el buzón	postbox
la cama	bed
la cocina	kitchen/cooker
el comedor	dining room
el correo	post
el cuarto	room
la chimenea	chimney/fireplace
el desván	attic
el dormitorio	bedroom
la ducha	shower
la escalera	stairs
el estante	shelf
el frigorífico	refrigerator
el garaje	garage
el hogar	hearth/home
el inodoro	toilet
el jardín	garden
la lámpara	lamp
el lavabo	washbasin
la puerta	door
la reja	railing/fence
la sala	sitting room
la silla	chair
el sillón	armchair
el sofá	sofa
el sótano	basement
el techo	roof
el televisor	TV set
el timbre	doorbell
la ventana	window
la verja	gate
los animales de casa	pets
la araña	spider
el canario	canary
el conejo	rabbit
el gato	cat
el hámster	hamster
el pájaro	bird
el perro	dog
el pez	fish
el ratón	mouse

Expressions

¿Dónde están...?	Where are...?
¿Qué son?	What are they?
en casa	at home

Grammar

- the verb *estar* (to be):

yo estoy	I am
tú estás	you are (sing. inform.)
usted está	you are (sing. form.)
él/ella está	he/she/it is
nosotros/as estamos	we are
vosotros/as estáis	you are (pl. inform.)
ustedes están	you are (pl. form.)
ellos/ellas están	they are

- more prepositions of place: *fuera de* (outside), *dentro de* (inside), *detrás de* (behind), *delante de* (in front of), *entre* (between)

Teaching ideas

Picture dictionary
Use an enlarged copy of the Picture dictionary on pages 48 and 49 to display in the classroom for reference. Ask the children to write the Spanish word for any of the featured items not shown in the dictionary around the border. They could draw additional items in the rooms and label them in Spanish.

Practise prepositions of place by asking where the characters in the Picture dictionary are. To revise the words for pets, ask the children to draw the pets in different places in the house. To revise numbers and plurals, ask the question *¿Cuántos/as ... hay?* To focus on the verbs, ask questions such as *¿Quién come?* (Who is eating?), *¿Dónde come?* (Where is he or she eating?)

Spanish culture
Discuss the different types of houses that people live in. Use the pull-out frieze to talk about traditional Spanish houses. Pictures or postcards of places and cities in Spain act as good visual aids.

As is the case in most large cities, many people in Spain live in flats. The Spanish word for a flat is *el piso*.

Ask the children to create signs with the sayings *Hogar dulce hogar* (Home, sweet home) and *Mi casa es tu casa* (My house is your house) to display at home.

Notes on the activities

Page 42 Fuera de la casa Copy the activity sheet onto A3 card to introduce the words for the external parts of a house and objects found outside. When the children are comfortable with the vocabulary and have completed the activity sheet, review the prepositions of place by asking questions such as *¿Dónde está el perro?* (Where is the dog?)

Page 43 Los cuartos de la casa Make an enlarged copy of this page and explain that this shows the inside of the house on page 42. Present the words for the rooms by asking *¿Qué es?* while pointing to different parts of the house. Prompt the answer by saying *Es la cocina/Es la escalera*, etc. Put the children into pairs and ask them to repeat the same speaking activity with their partner. Once the children have become familiar with the words for items of furniture and household objects shown on page 44, they could use this page to play *Veo, veo* (I spy) in pairs using letters of the alphabet to identify the contents of the rooms shown:

A: *Veo, veo.*
B: *¿Qué ves?*
A: *Veo una cosa que empieza con la 'a'.*
B: *¿La alfombra?*
A: *¡No!*
B: *¿El armario?*
A: *¡Sí!*

For a more challenging game, allow the children 10 minutes beforehand to look up the words for objects shown in the rooms on this page but not named on page 44. They could order the new words alphabetically and then check the letter of the alphabet chosen against the words on their lists as they play.

Page 44 Dentro de los cuartos Present the words for furniture and fittings by copying the flashcards onto A3 card. Ask *¿Qué es?* while holding up a card. Prompt the answer by saying *Es la bañera/Es el sillón*, etc. Put the children into pairs and ask them to repeat the speaking activity with their partner. They could also play Snap! with a set of cards cut from two copies of the sheet. Instead of saying 'Snap!' when two cards with the same picture appear, they should say the Spanish word on the card. Some children might be able to identify the pictures with the words masked. As an additional activity ask the children to colour-code the flashcard labels according to gender.

Page 45 Los animales de casa Use enlarged copies of the animal drawings to introduce the words for pets. Include *gato*, *perro* and *pájaro* from page 42. As a further oral comprehension activity, ask the children to draw more pets on the sheet by giving instructions like *Dibuja un conejo delante del frigorífico* (Draw a rabbit in front of the fridge) or *Dibuja dos ratones sobre el sillón* (Draw two mice on the armchair). The children could conduct a class survey of what pets their classmates have and display the results in a chart on the wall. As an extension ask them if they know the names of any other animals. They will enjoy hearing the sounds that animals make in Spanish and comparing them with their English equivalents. Examples might include: *los perros dicen guau guau*; *los gatos dicen miau*; *las vacas dicen muuu*; *los patos dicen cuá cuá*; *las ovejas dicen bee*; *el gallo dice kikirikí*; *la gallina dice cocorocó*; *los pollitos dicen pío pío*.

Page 46 ¡Mira con atención! As an introduction to this activity, place the enlarged pet drawings from page 45 around the classroom and ask the children questions such as *¿Dónde está el hámster?* (Where is the hamster?) Prompt them to reply with the right preposition of place and classroom object. As a further extension activity correct the remaining false sentences either orally or in writing.

Page 47 ¿Dónde están todos? This activity provides practice of the verb *estar* (to be). Go over all of the personal pronouns and the conjugation of *estar* (see previous page) before completing the sheet. Ask the children to write the correct pronoun in front of each form of the verb in the word list. Discuss the differences between *tú* (informal) and *usted* (formal) and between the masculine and feminine forms of the personal pronouns *él/ella*, *nosotros/nosotras*, *vosotros/vosotras* and *ellos/ellas*. Point out that one of the differences between *ser* and *estar* is that *estar* is used to indicate where people and objects are located. As a further extension, invite a child to place him or herself in a different part of the classroom (behind the door, under a bookshelf). Ask the class *¿Dónde está …?* Prompt the children to answer correctly. Repeat the activity with other individuals or pairs of children to practise the plural forms of the verb.

Fuera de la casa

Mira la lista.

Escribe las palabras.

Lista

el buzón
la chimenea
el garaje
el jardín
la puerta
la reja
el techo
el timbre
la ventana
la verja

Translation: ***Outside the house****. Look at the list. Write the words.*

Teachers' note: This activity sheet introduces words relating to the exterior of a house. Go over the word bank vocabulary with the children to ensure correct pronunciation. Remind them to write the noun for each part of the house along with its corresponding article.

Los cuartos de la casa

Mira la lista.
Escribe las palabras.

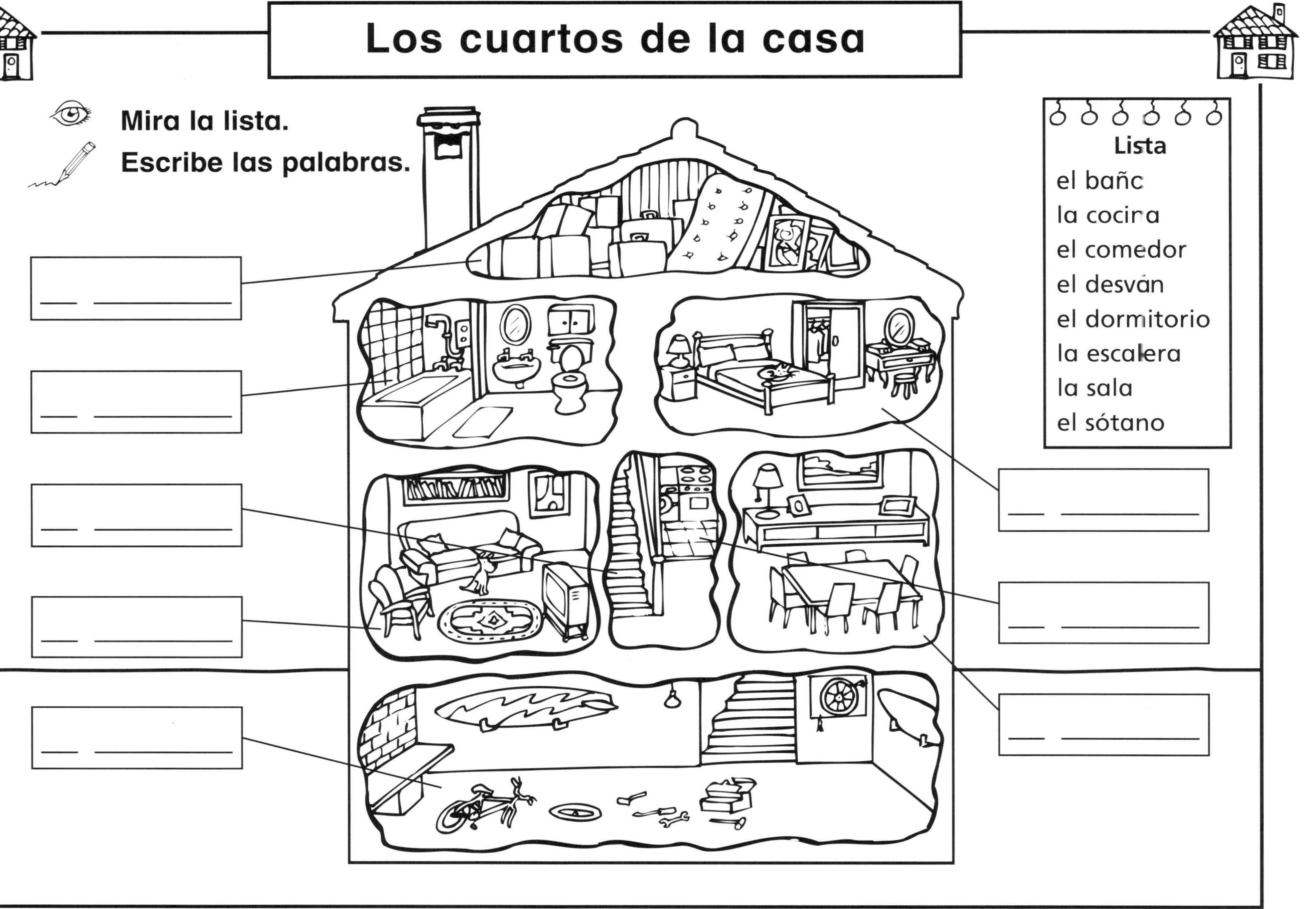

Lista
el baño
la cocina
el comedor
el desván
el dormitorio
la escalera
la sala
el sótano

Translation: ***Rooms of the house.*** *Look at the list. Write the words.*
Teachers' note: Enlarge the sheet to A3 if desired. This activity introduces the rooms of the house shown on page 42. Go over the vocabulary with the children to make sure they know how to pronounce each word correctly. Ensure that they write the noun for each part of the house along with its corresponding article.

Dentro de los cuartos

Corta las palabras.

Pega las palabras debajo de los dibujos.

el inodoro	el lavabo	el frigorífico	la lámpara
la cocina	la cama	la ducha	la silla
la alfombra	el sillón	el armario	la bañera
el estante	el sofá	la mesa	el televisor

Translation: ***Inside the rooms.*** *Cut out the words. Glue the words under the pictures.*
Teachers' note: Copy the sheet onto A3 card to make flashcards. This activity introduces the words for furniture and fittings inside the house. Point out that the word *cocina* means both 'kitchen' (page 43) and 'cooker' (this page). Ask the children to match the pictures and labels before gluing each label in its correct place. To practise the words they could play Snap! or Pairs with cards cut from two copies of the sheet.

Los animales de casa

Lee.

Dibuja los animales.

el pez	el canario	el ratón	el hámster	el conejo	la araña

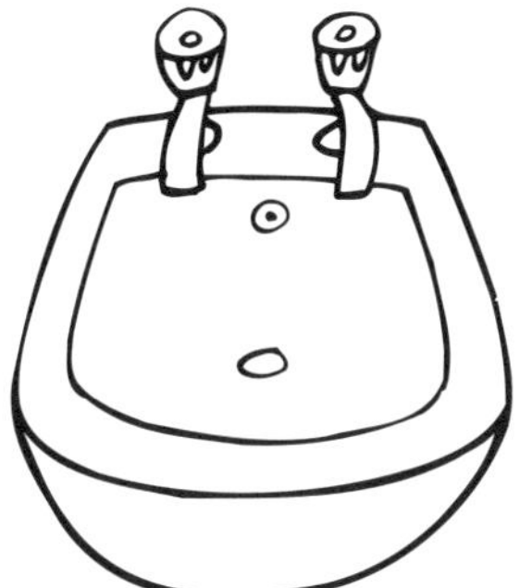 El pez está en el lavabo.	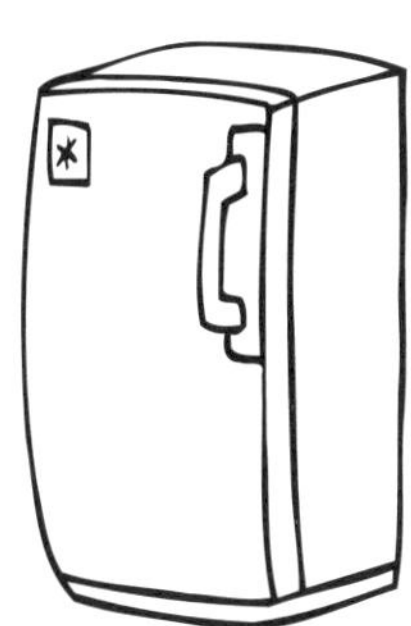 La araña está sobre el frigorífico.	 El conejo está debajo del sillón.
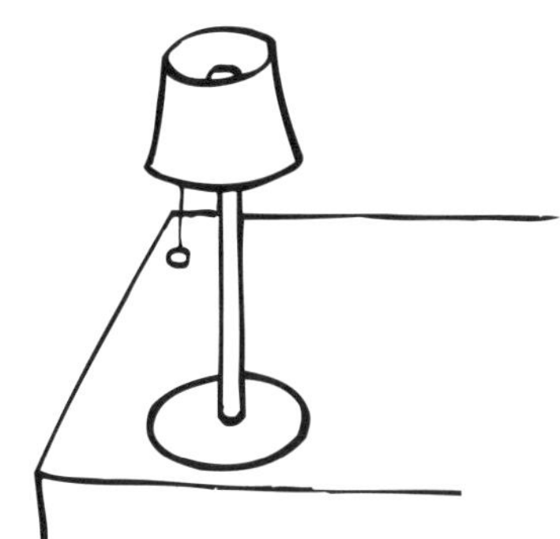 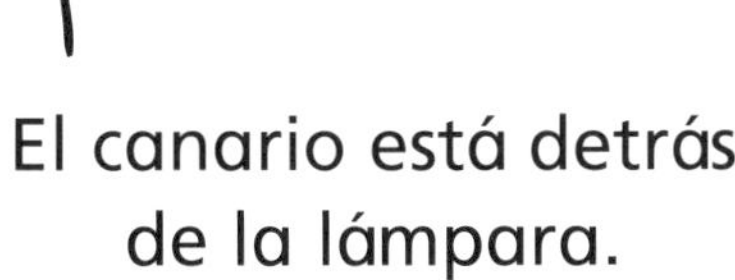 El canario está detrás de la lámpara.	 El ratón está delante de la cocina.	 El hámster está entre la silla y la mesa.

Y ahora

Practica el diálogo.

¿Dónde está el ratón?

El ratón está delante de la cocina.

Translation: *Pets. Read. Draw the animals. • Practise the dialogue.*
Teachers' note: This activity introduces the words for pets and revises furniture and fittings and prepositions of place. The children should read each sentence and draw the animal in the correct position. For the extension activity the children should keep changing the question, referring to each of the drawings in turn.

¡Mira con atención!

Mira el dibujo.

Marca verdadero ✔ o falso ✘.

1 El hámster está entre la bañera y el lavabo. ☐

2 La abuela está en la sala. ☐

3 Marta está fuera de la casa. ☐

4 Carlos está delante del frigorífico. ☐

5 El pez está sobre el estante. ☐

6 El ratón está debajo de la alfombra. ☐

7 La araña está dentro del armario. ☐

8 El abuelo está detrás de la mesa. ☐

Y ahora

Escribe dos de las frases falsas de forma correcta.

Translation: ***Look carefully!*** *Look at the picture. Mark true or false. • Write the correct form of two of the false sentences.*

Teachers' note: This reading activity revises pet names, house vocabulary and prepositions of place. It requires the children to read the sentences, look at the picture and mark true or false in the boxes. For the extension activity the children can choose to correct any two of the five false sentences.

¿Dónde están todos?

Mira la lista.

Completa las frases.

Lista

estoy	está	están
estás	estamos	están
está	estáis	

Tú ___________ en casa.

Yo ___________ en el garaje.

Él ___________ detrás de la puerta.

Usted ___________ en el jardín.

Ellas ___________ delante de la verja.

Ustedes ___________ en la sala.

Nosotros ___________ en el jardín.

Vosotras ___________ detrás del sofá.

Y ahora

¿Dónde estás tú?

Dibuja.

Escribe.

Translation: *Where is everybody? Look at the list. Complete the sentences.* • *Where are you? Draw. Write.*
Teachers' note: This activity sheet practises the present tense of the verb *estar* (to be). Remind the children that *estar* is used to express where objects are located. For the extension activity invite them to read their answer aloud.

Picture dictionary

En casa

ver la televisión
cocinar
dormir
comer
el frigorífico
el jardín
el balcón
la mesa
la silla
el armario
la cama

Topic 5: Al aire libre

Key vocabulary

al aire libre	outdoors
bailar	to dance
caminar	to walk
correr	to run
escalar	to mountain-climb
esquiar	to ski
hacer el pino	to do a handstand
hacer una voltereta	to do a somersault
hacer monopatín	to skateboard
hacer snowboard	to snowboard
hacer un castillo de arena	to make a sandcastle
jugar al baloncesto, al frisbi, al fútbol, al golf, al tenis	to play basketball, frisbee, football, golf, tennis
montar en bicicleta	to ride a bicycle
montar a caballo	to ride a horse
nadar	to swim
patinar	to skate
patinar sobre hielo	to ice-skate
pescar	to fish
saltar	to jump
saltar a la cuerda	to skip
saltar con un pie	to hop
trepar	to climb

numbers 11 to 30: *once* (11), *doce* (12), *trece* (13), *catorce* (14), *quince* (15), *dieciséis* (16), *diecisiete* (17), *dieciocho* (18), *diecinueve* (19), *veinte* (20), *veintiuno* (21), *veintidós* (22), *veintitrés* (23), *veinticuatro* (24), *veinticinco* (25), *veintiséis* (26), *veintisiete* (27), *veintiocho* (28), *veintinueve* (29), *treinta* (30)

Expressions

¡Vamos a...!	Let's...
¡Buena idea!	Good idea!
¡No! (Mejor) vamos a...	No! (Instead) let's...
La actividad preferida de ... es ...	...'s favourite activity is...
Mi actividad preferida es...	My favourite activity is...
¿Sabes...?	Can you...?
¿Cuánto es ... más/menos ...?	How much is ... plus/minus ...?

Grammar

- the verb *saber* (to know/be able to):

yo sé	I know/can
tú sabes	you know/can
él/ella sabe	he/she knows/can

Teaching ideas

Classroom routine

As part of your daily routine, spend at least five minutes practising numbers. Use drills and maths problems until the children are familiar with them: for example, call out a number and ask them to say the number that comes *antes* (before) or *después* (after).

This topic introduces many new verbs. Use mime as a means of helping the children to work out their meaning. If you have introduced the three types of verb: *-ar*, *-er* and *-ir* verbs, ask the children to sort their flashcards according to the verb ending. Discuss how Spanish verbs have a stem and an ending. Use a few familiar verbs as models: for example, *cocin-ar* (to cook), *com-er* (to eat), *dorm-ir* (to sleep).

Vocabulary note

Discuss how languages are alive and influence each other. In this topic *tenis*, *fútbol* and *frisbi* come from English but have undergone a spelling change; *hacer snowboard* (to snowboard) and *hacer surf* (to surf) use the English word and spelling – although the pronunciation is often 'spanglished'.

Picture dictionary

The Picture dictionary on pages 60 and 61 features general outdoor activities and a playground. The dictionary around the border does not include all of the sports and activities from the topic. Ask the children to label those activities in the picture which have no accompanying entry. To revise numbers and plurals, ask questions starting *¿Cuántos/as ... hay?* (How many ... are there?) To focus on the verbs, ask questions such as *¿Quién hace monopatín?* (Who is skateboarding?) To focus on the adjectives, ask questions like *¿Quién está cansado/a?* (Who is tired?)

Spanish culture

Football is the most popular sport in Spain. Ask the children if they know the names of any Spanish football teams (for example, Real Madrid, Barcelona, Atlético Madrid, Valencia) and players (for example, Raúl , Joaquín, Xavi). Talk about the colour of their strip and different players' shirt numbers. Other popular sports in Spain are tennis and Formula 1 motor racing. Can the children name any famous Spanish tennis players (for example, Rafael Nadal – French Open champion 2005 and 2006) or drivers (for example, Fernando Alonso, winner of the 2005 and 2006 championships)?

Notes on the activities

Page 52 De once a treinta Revise the numbers from 0 to 10. Introduce the numbers from 11 to 30 with enlarged copies of the number cards. Prompt the children to repeat the numbers by counting *de dos en dos* (in twos), *de tres en tres* (in threes), etc. Call out a number and ask them to show you the correct card. The children could play *¡Guerra!* (War!) with their two sets of flashcards (0–30). Put the class into pairs. Each child places the set of cards face-down. Both children must take the top card from their set and place it on the table, face-up, at the same time. Whoever puts down the highest number calls out the number and takes both cards. The player who manages to gain both sets of cards wins.

Page 53 Contemos Practise numbers by asking the children to do maths calculations using *más* (plus) and *menos* (minus). Pose questions such as *¿Cuánto es diez más once menos dos?* (How many is 10 plus 11 minus 2?) Make the maths calculation longer and longer to make it more challenging. As a follow-up to the extension activity, say a number and ask the children to tell you as quickly as possible the number that comes before or after it.

Page 54 Saltar y correr Use mime or play *Simón dice* (Simon says) to practise the action verbs. When the children are familiar with the new words, play the following version of Pelmanism (Pairs): on the back of each card write a number from 1 to 24 with a thick felt-tip pen. Tape the flashcards onto the blackboard with the numbers facing the class. Prompt a child to say two numbers aloud in Spanish to try and match a word and its drawing. Lift the two cards to see if they match. Repeat with other children until all the cards have been matched. If they are ready, introduce the plural command form of the verb: for example, *¡Corred!* (Run!) The children should mime the corresponding action.

Page 55 ¡Vamos a jugar! To introduce the expression *¡Vamos a …!* call out two or more children and invite them to mime with you the action you say: for example, *¡Vamos a nadar!* (Let's swim!) Prompt them to reply enthusiastically *¡Sí, vamos!* (Yes, let's!) or *¡Buena idea!* (Good idea!) Then ask them to reply negatively and to propose something else: for example, *¡No, mejor vamos a patinar!* (No, let's go skating instead!) As a further extension, the children can practise the ***Y ahora*** dialogue using the flashcards from page 54. Divide the class into pairs. Each child should place a set of cards face-up on the desk. The children take turns to pick up a card, showing the picture to their partner and proposing the activity. Their partner should reply negatively, pick up a card from their own set and suggest that activity.

Page 56 Las actividades preferidas Start by picking up a flashcard from page 54; show it to the class and say, for example, *Mi actividad preferida es caminar* (My favourite activity is walking). Emphasise *Mi* (My) with your voice and *preferida* (favourite) with a thumbs-up sign. Ask a child *¿Cuál es tu actividad preferida?* (What's your favourite activity?) Emphasise *tu* (your) with your voice and by gesturing towards the child. Prompt the child to reply: for example, *Mi actividad preferida es correr* (My favourite activity is running). After the children have completed the sheet go over the answers by asking *¿Cuál es la actividad preferida de Isabel?* (What is Isabel's favourite activity?) and so on.

Page 57 Más actividades afuera After introducing the new vocabulary and practising its pronunciation, focus on the activity verbs according to how they are structured. Discuss the verbs *jugar/montar* + preposition: for example, *jugar al baloncesto*, *montar a caballo*; *hacer* + noun: for example, *hacer snowboard*; and verbs that stand alone: for example, *escalar*. Ask the children to sort the flashcards, and those from page 54, into these categories. When all the vocabulary has been learned, assess oral comprehension by asking questions such as *¿Qué actividades se hacen en el invierno/verano?* (Which activities are done in winter/summer?), *¿Qué actividades se hacen individualmente, en grupo/equipo, con un balón…?* (Which activities are done alone, in a group/team, with a ball…?)

Page 58 Yo sé… Using the flashcards from pages 54 and 57 introduce the verb *saber* by showing an activity card and saying *Yo sé/no sé escalar* (I can/cannot climb). Repeat with other flashcards. Add a brief comment such as *Escalar es fácil/difícil* (Climbing is easy/difficult) to emphasise your ability/inability to do the activity. Explain that *saber* actually means 'to know' but is used in this context to mean 'to know how to' or 'to be able to'. After the children have grasped the meaning of *Yo sé*, introduce the question *¿Sabes hacer el pino?* (Can you do a handstand?) Invite the children to draw up a survey and interview each other. Create a poster to display the results in the classroom.

Page 59 ¿Sabes patinar? Introduce the third person of *saber* by using mime. Ask a volunteer *¿Sabes saltar a la cuerda?* (Can you skip?) After he or she has replied, report back to the class: *… sabe/no sabe saltar a la cuerda*. Emphasise the verb with your voice and mime. Some children could exchange their completed sheets with a partner and orally report the ***Y ahora*** sentences in the third person.

De once a treinta

Corta las fichas.

once	doce	trece	catorce
quince	dieciséis	diecisiete	dieciocho
diecinueve	veinte	veintiuno	veintidós
veintitrés	veinticuatro	veinticinco	veintiséis
veintisiete	veintiocho	veintinueve	treinta

Translation: ***From 11 to 30.*** *Cut out the cards.*
Teachers' note: To make flashcards copy the sheet onto A3 card. This activity sheet introduces the numbers from 11 to 30 and helps the children to become familiar with their written form. Ask them to put the cards in numerical order and practise the pronunciation. They can then write the number in figures on either the front or the back of the cards. Use the cards to play *¡Guerra!* (War!) (see **Notes on the activities**, page 51).

Contemos

Mira el dibujo.

Completa las frases.

Lista

catorce
dieciséis
quince
seis
veintisiete

Hay cuatro caballos.

Hay ________ perros.

Hay ________ pájaros en el cielo.

Hay ____________ pájaros y patos.

Hay __________ peces y tortugas.

Hay __________ animales en el agua.

Escribe los números que vienen antes y después.

___________ diecinueve ___________

___________ veinticuatro ___________

Translation: ***Let's count****. Look at the picture. Complete the sentences. • Write the numbers that come before and after.*

Teachers' note: This activity gives practice in using the numbers 0 to 30. The children should count the animals and write the number in word form to complete the sentences. Encourage them to look up unfamiliar words in a dictionary. The numbers in the extension activity should also be written as words.

Saltar y correr

Corta las fichas.

	caminar		jugar al fútbol
montar en bicicleta		nadar	
 	montar a caballo		patinar
bailar		correr	
 	trepar		jugar al tenis
saltar a la cuerda		pescar	

Translation: ***Jumping and running****. Cut out the cards.*

Teachers' note: Copy the sheet onto A3 card. These flashcards introduce verbs for outdoor activities. The children could glue the word to the back of the picture or they could use the cards to play Pelmanism (Pairs) by matching the word and the drawing (see **Notes on the activities**, page 51).

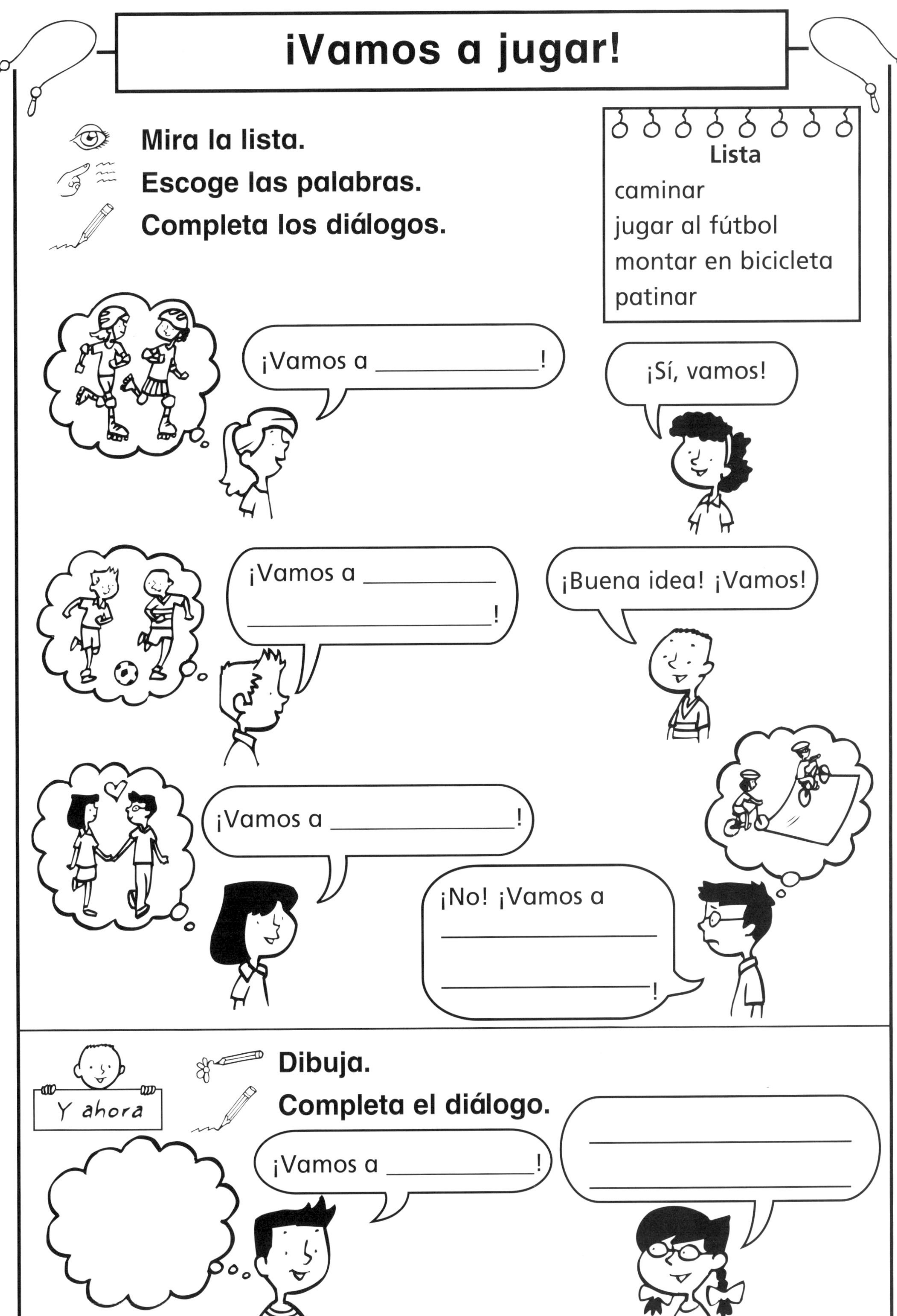

¡Vamos a jugar!
Mira la lista.
Escoge las palabras.
Completa los diálogos.
Lista
caminar
jugar al fútbol
montar en bicicleta
patinar
¡Vamos a ______!
¡Sí, vamos!
¡Vamos a ______ ______!
¡Buena idea! ¡Vamos!
¡Vamos a ______!
¡No! ¡Vamos a ______ ______!
Y ahora
Dibuja.
Completa el diálogo.
¡Vamos a ______!

Translation: ***Let's go and play!*** *Look at the list. Choose the words. Complete the dialogues. • Draw. Complete the dialogue.*

Teachers' note: This activity sheet combines the expression *¡Vamos a…!* (Let's…) with the infinitive form of the verb to form an invitation. It also practises an affirmative and a negative reply. For the extension activity the children should draw an activity in the thought bubble, then complete the dialogue.

Las actividades preferidas

Mira la lista.

Completa las frases.

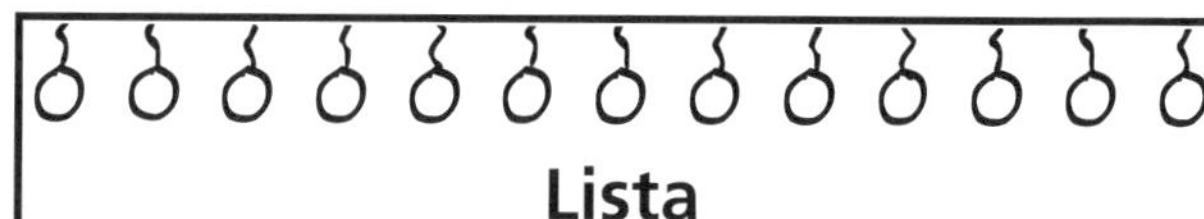

Lista

actividad	preferida
montar a caballo	nadar
saltar a la cuerda	trepar

Isabel

La actividad preferida de

Isabel es ______________________.

Jorge

La actividad preferida de

Jorge es ______________________.

Patricia

La actividad preferida de

Patricia es ______________________.

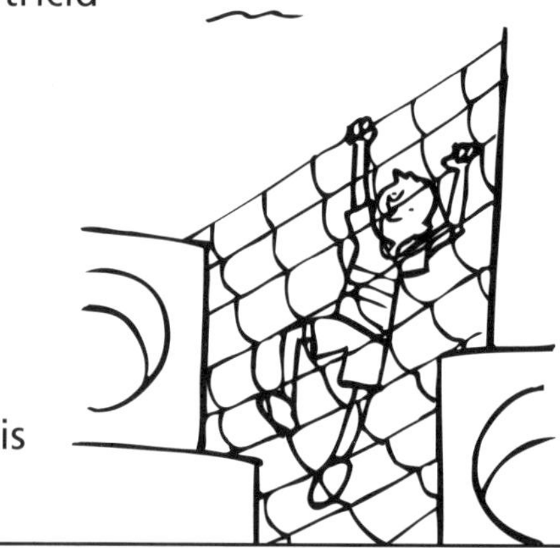

Luis

La ______________ ______________ de

Luis es ______________________.

Dibuja tu actividad preferida.

Escribe una frase.

Translation: ***Favourite activities***. *Look at the list. Complete the sentences. • Draw your favourite activity. Write a sentence..*

Teachers' note: This activity sheet gives practice in expressing what other people like to do. The four sentences in the activity follow the same sentence structure. Each blank line represents one word. The extension activity prompts the children to express their own personal preference.

Más actividades afuera

 **Corta las palabras.**

 **Pega las palabras debajo de los dibujos.**

saltar con un pie	jugar al baloncesto	hacer un castillo de arena	escalar
hacer el pino	patinar sobre hielo	hacer snowboard	jugar al frisbi
jugar al golf	esquiar	hacer monopatín	hacer una voltereta

Translation: ***More outdoor activities.*** *Cut out the words. Glue the words under the pictures.*
Teachers' note: Copy the sheet onto A3 card. These flashcards introduce more verbs for outdoor activities. Ask the children to match the pictures and the words before gluing the words onto the pictures. To help them to learn the vocabulary, invite them to mime the actions by playing *Simón dice* (Simon says) as a group and then to play Snap! in pairs.

Yo sé...

 **Mira los dibujos.**

 **Lee las frases.**

 **Escribe los nombres.**

Yo sé escalar pero no sé jugar al baloncesto. ________________

Yo sé escalar y patinar sobre hielo. ________________

Yo sé hacer el pino pero no sé hacer monopatín. ________________

Practica el diálogo.

Y ahora
¿Sabes saltar a la cuerda?
No, no sé saltar a la cuerda.

Translation: ***I can...*** *Look at the pictures. Read the sentences. Write the names. • Practise the dialogue.*
Teachers' note: This activity introduces the first and second persons singular of the verb *saber* (to know/be able) to express skill and revises outdoor activities. It combines a reading comprehension exercise with interpreting data to assess the children's understanding of the vocabulary and the constructions *Yo sé/no sé*. They can practise the dialogue by referring to the pictures or by using their cards from pages 54 and 57.

¿Sabes patinar?

Lee las frases.

Escribe ✔ o ✘.

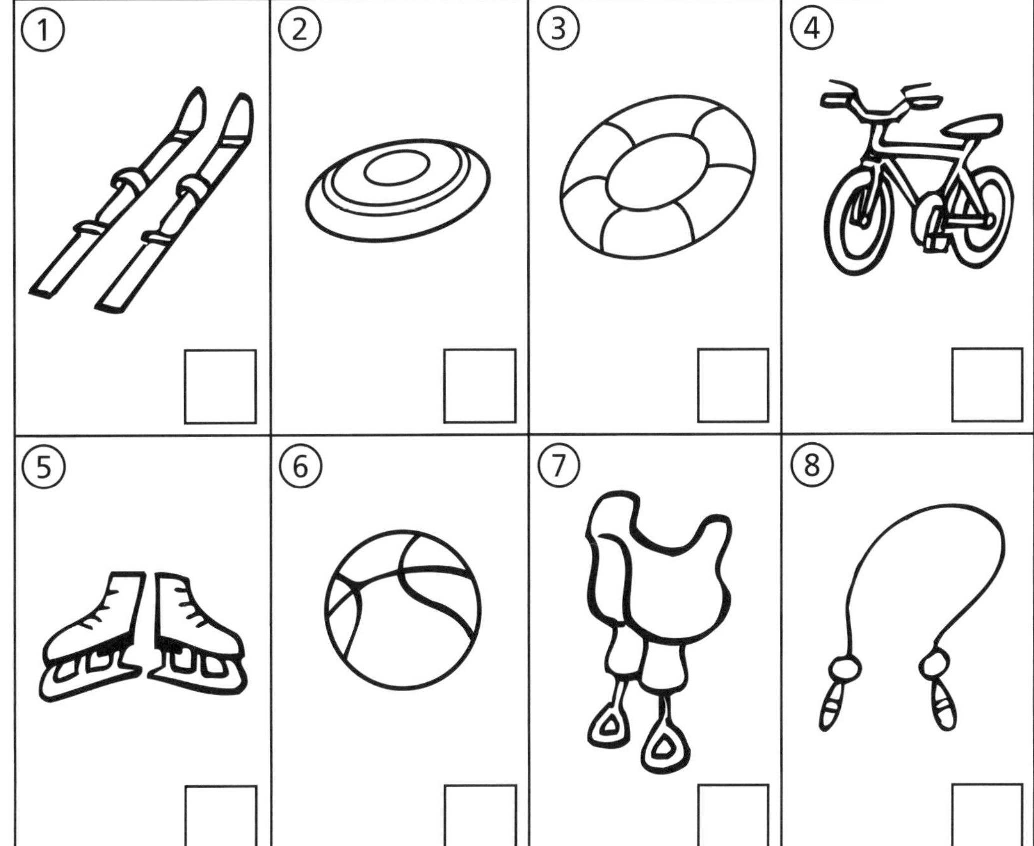

Carlos

Carlos sabe patinar sobre hielo.

Carlos no sabe esquiar.

Carlos no sabe saltar a la cuerda.

Carlos sabe nadar.

Carlos sabe jugar al frisbi.

Carlos no sabe jugar al baloncesto.

Carlos no sabe montar a caballo.

Carlos sabe montar en bicicleta.

Completa con sé **o** no sé.

Yo ______________ jugar al fútbol.

Yo ______________ patinar sobre hielo.

Yo ______________ pescar.

Yo ______________ montar en bicicleta.

Translation: *Can you skate? Read the sentences. Write a tick or a cross. • Complete with* sé *or* no sé.
Teachers' note: This activity introduces the third person singular of the verb *saber* (to know/be able). The children read and then match written information with equipment associated with different activities. For the extension activity the children should write whether or not they are able to do the activities. Encourage them to read their answers aloud.

Picture dictionary

¡Vamos afuera!

triste

contento/a

cansado/a

saltar

caer

el equipo

montar a caballo

patinar

nadar

montar en bicicleta

correr

Recommended resources

Teaching materials

Primary Spanish Starter Pack 1: 'Tú y yo' and Continuation Pack 2: 'Mi ciudad y mi colegio' by Ilsa Rowe and Ian Killbery, published by Early Start Languages – Primary Modern Languages Diversification Project, 7 Clanwilliam Road, Deal, Kent CT14 7BX, www.earlystart.co.uk. Resource pack with DVD/video and guide for non-specialist teachers.

Workbooks

Spanish for Beginners Pack by Angela Wilkes and John Shackell, published by Usborne, 2004. Pack contains book, workbook, sticker dictionary, flashcards, audio tape and Internet links.

Dictionaries

Spanish Dictionary for Beginners by Helen Davies and John Shackell, published by Usborne, 2002.

DK First Spanish Picture Dictionary published by Dorling Kindersley, 2005.

Oxford Spanish Dictionary: Spanish–English, English–Spanish by Beatriz Galimberti Jarman, Roy Russell, Carol Styles Carvajal, Jane Horwood, published by Oxford University Press, 2003.

Websites for teachers

www.bbc.co.uk/languages/spanish
Hear Spanish spoken and test your Spanish using simple games, vocabulary and grammar exercises. There is a specific link for primary school Spanish teachers and children.

www.cnice.mecd.es/ninos
Links directory compiled by the Spanish Ministry of Education and Science. In Spanish.

www.cvc.cervantes.es
Material for Spanish-language teachers and students. Up-to-date information about cultural events. Offers an interactive page for children. In Spanish.

www.guiainfantil.com
Spanish website for parents, teachers and carers. A good resource for cultural information, songs, stories, etc.

www.ihmadrid.com/comunicativo
Spanish-language resources, activities, lesson plans, self-correcting grammar exercises.

www.sgci.mec.es/uk
Spanish Embassy site with details about Spanish education and culture. Links to *Tecla*, an online magazine for Spanish-language teachers and learners.

Websites for children

www.bbc.co.uk/schools/primaryspanish/index.shtml
Fun online Spanish-language activities for children. There is also a section with tips for Spanish teachers.

www.milcuentos.com
Spanish website with children's stories, including audio.

www.pdictionary.com
Multilingual Internet picture dictionary.

Curriculum information and teaching methods

The Department of Education and Skills
Modern Foreign Language Team
Sanctuary Buildings, Area 4D
London SW1P 3BT
tel: 020 7925 6291
e-mail: MFL.team@dfes.gsi.gov.uk
website: www.dfes.gov.uk/languages

The National Centre for Languages (CILT)
20 Bedfordbury
London WC2N 4LB
tel: 020 7379 5101
e-mail: info@cilt.org.uk
website: www.cilt.org.uk

The National Advisory Centre on Early Language Learning (NACELL)
20 Bedfordbury
London WC2N 4LB
tel: 020 7379 5101 Ext. 286
e-mail: nacell@cilt.org.uk
website: www.nacell.org.uk

The Qualifications and Curriculum Authority (QCA)
83 Piccadilly
London W1J 8QA
tel: 020 7509 5555
e-mail: info@qca.org.uk
website: www.qca.org.uk

Suppliers of books and teaching materials

Bilingual Supplies for Children
PO Box 4081
Bournemouth
Dorset BH8 9ZZ
website: www.bilingual-supplies.co.uk

Early Start Languages
74 Middle Deal Road
Kent CT14 9RH
tel: 01304 362 569
e-mail: orders@earlystart.co.uk
website: www.earlystart.co.uk

European Schoolbooks Limited
The Runnings
Cheltenham
Gloucestershire GL51 9PQ
tel: 01242 245252
e-mail: direct@esb.co.uk
website: www.eurobooks.co.uk

The European Bookshop
5 Warwick Street
London W1B 5LU
tel: 020 7734 5259
e-mail: mrg@esb.co.uk

Answers

p11

llamo — *¡Hola! Yo me llamo*
Hasta luego — *Adiós*

p12

Buenos días
Buenas tardes
Buenas noches
Buenas noches

p13

Yo soy niña. — *Yo soy niño.*
Yo soy chica. — *Yo soy chico.*
Yo soy mujer. — *Yo soy hombre.*

p14

C	B	O	R	M	O	R	A	D	O
E	M	R	O	J	O	V	V	N	B
L	M	G	S	S	K	Ñ	E	E	L
E	A	R	A	Z	U	L	R	G	A
S	R	I	D	C	Y	Z	D	R	N
T	R	S	O	J	Q	L	E	O	C
E	Ó	A	M	A	R	I	L	L	O
B	N	A	R	A	N	J	A	E	P

p19

Hay cuatro mesas.
Hay dos estuches.
Hay tres reglas.
Hay siete libros.

p20

tengo
tiene
tienes
tiene

p21

debajo de
sobre
en

p23

¿Puedo ir al baño, por favor? — *No entiendo.*
¿Puedo ir a beber agua, por favor? — *No sé.*
Perdón — *¡Lo siento!*

p24

Y ahora

geografía — *historia*
educación física — *inglés*
informática — *matemáticas*
música — *español*

The hidden word is *¡Perfecto!*

p25

Es aburrida.
Es difícil.
Es divertida.

p30

Mi hermana se llama Mariana. — *Mi padre se llama Gustavo.*
Mi abuela se llama Lucía. — *Mi abuelo se llama Ernesto.*
Mi hermano se llama Pablo. — *Mi madre se llama Pilar.*

p31

Adriana es la hija de Alberto y Gracia.
Gabriel es el abuelo de Carlos.
Gracia es la madre de Adriana, Carlos y Jaime.

Y ahora

verdadero
falso
verdadero
verdadero

p33

abuela
tío
primo
tía
prima
nieta

p35

La abuela de Carlos es vieja.
El padre de Carlos es alto.
El abuelo de Carlos es viejo.
Yo soy joven.
La hermana de Carlos es simpática.
El abuelo de Carlos es bajo.
El hermano de Carlos es joven.
La madre de Carlos es joven y alta.

p36

Él se llama Alfonso García.
La prima de Raúl es alta.
Yo soy hijo único.

p37

María	*E*	*Margarita*	*C*
José	*G*	*Choco*	*D*
Clara	*B*	*Felipe*	*A*
Inés	*F*		

p46

1 *Verdadero*
2 *Verdadero*
3 *Falso*
4 *Falso*
5 *Falso*
6 *Verdadero*
7 *Falso*
8 *Falso*

Y ahora

3 *Marta está en el dormitorio.*
4 *Carlos está detrás del frigorífico.*
5 *El pez está sobre el televisor.*
7 *La araña está sobre el armario.*
8 *El abuelo está detrás de la silla.*

p47

Tú estás en casa.
Yo estoy en el garaje.
Él está detrás de la puerta.
Usted está en el jardín.
Ellas están delante de la verja.
Ustedes están en la sala.
Nosotros estamos en el jardín.
Vosotras estáis detrás del sofá.

p53

seis
quince
veintisiete
catorce
dieciséis

Y ahora

dieciocho *veinte*
veintitrés *veinticinco*

p55

¡Vamos a patinar!
¡Vamos a jugar al fútbol!
¡Vamos a caminar! *¡No! ¡Vamos a montar en bicicleta!*

p56

La actividad preferida de Isabel es saltar a la cuerda.
La actividad preferida de Jorge es montar a caballo.
La actividad preferida de Patricia es nadar.
La actividad preferida de Luis es trepar.

p58

Elisa
Paula
Jorge

p59

1 ✘	**2** ✔	**3** ✔	**4** ✔
5 ✔	**6** ✘	**7** ✘	**8** ✘